P9-CSB-283

THE HART HOUSE COLLECTION OF CANADIAN PAINTINGS

JEREMY ADAMSON

THE HART HOUSE COLLECTION OF Canadian Paintings

Published in association with the Art Committee
of Hart House by University of Toronto Press

Printed in Canada
SBN 8020 4022 5

This book
was designed by
WILLIAM RUETER
under the direction of
ALLAN FLEMING
and was printed by
University of
Toronto
Press

The Prayer of the Founders is that Hart House, under the guidance of its Warden, may serve in the generations to come the highest interests of this University by drawing into a common fellowship the members of the several Colleges and Faculties, and by gathering into a true society the teacher and the student, the graduate and the undergraduate; further, that the members of Hart House may discover within its walls the true education that is to be found in good fellowship, in friendly disputation and debate, in the conversation of wise and earnest men, in music, pictures and the play, in the casual book, in sports and games and the mastery of the body; and lastly, that just as in the days of war this House was devoted to the training in arms of the young soldier, so, in the time of peace its halls may be dedicated to the task of arming youth with strength and suppleness of limb, with clarity of mind and depth of understanding, and with a spirit of true religion and high endeavour.

Foreword

HUGO MCPHERSON
Commissioner and Chairman
The National Film Board of Canada

In 1924 Paul Klee told a student audience in Jena that a true artist must believe "that the process of creation can today hardly be complete ... He sees the act of world creation stretching from the past to the future. Genesis eternal!" A similar mood of excitement and experiment must have inspired the students, faculty and the then Warden of Hart House, J. Burgon Bickersteth, when they began collecting *avant garde* painting – particularly the work of the Group of Seven – after World War I. But the collection was inspired by a second motive: Hart House began as an imposing and beautiful "club", in the English sense, for the male undergraduates, graduates and faculty of the University of Toronto; as such it provided all the amenities of dining rooms, squash courts, music rooms, a theatre, a library, a swimming pool, and a nonsectarian chapel. In such neo-Gothic setting an art collection had to be thought of, and to his undying credit Mr. Bickersteth recognized that this unique club – with fresh streams of members arriving every autumn and departing three or four years later – should not become a mausoleum for dubious portraits of governors, wardens, and stiff group-photographs of old boys. He therefore established an art committee which was responsible for acquisitions, hanging, and special exhibitions in the Hart House gallery.

In its subsequent history, I believe, this committee has achieved something of the alertness and imagination that Paul Klee demanded of the artist. I was fortunate enough to be chairman of the art committee for three sessions (1963–5), and I have known the collection since 1950. Now, without the least sense of *parti pris*, I am happy to make some observations on its development, its present, and its future.

The first and most obvious point to be made is that the collection is now sufficiently large and important to merit a new catalogue – a catalogue which at once gives readers a clear conception of the scope and vitality of the collection, and furnishes scholars and museum people with information essential to their work. Paintings from Hart House have been lent widely both in Canada and abroad; and as Canadian art develops, the demand for information on the holdings of the House will grow.

The second point of note is the unique and still developing manner in which the collection has been created. Funds have always been scarce, though successive Wardens and committees have been able to find special resources which made possible the purchase of particular paintings for the House. In the late thirties and the forties acquisitions were too often conservative – sincere but tedious beaux-arts reflections of the taste of upperclassmen or faculty of the day. Such lapses no doubt reflect the cultural temper of a particular generation. The significant point is that the art committee's developing independence – its appreciation of new modes and new forms of creation – has involved it increasingly in Canada's living art scene. In such a collection the accent must be contemporary, daring, and on occasion impolite.

The critical *gestalt* in the committee's growth, perhaps, was the decision in 1961 to buy a major canvas by Harold Town. The debate over this purchase was in some degree a struggle between traditional attitudes towards collecting and a desire for fresh expression. The *avant garde* forces carried the day, and in this decade the art committee behaves less as a solemn acquisitions committee than as a sponsor of new forces in Canadian art. I recall, for example, the opening of Les Levine's one-man show in 1964. Levine's curious flesh-coloured constructions of dismembered kitchen chairs sewn into vinyl skins could not be hung from the ceiling (screws in the ceiling were not *comme il faut*) so the works dangled from gibbet-like scaffolds hastily constructed for the occasion. And at the opening an electronic combo appeared and played jazz at a decibel volume that made the rafters of Hart House quiver. In a 1966 exhibition a corner of Dennis Burton's studio was reproduced in the Art Gallery as an environmental part of the artist's statement. (Those who objected were perhaps unaware that, years earlier, Brancusi's studio had become a permanent display in the Musée d'Art Contemporain in Paris.)

In the same vein, the art committee has become involved in arts festivals, film showings, and multi-media "happenings". It has recognized, in short, that art is *now*; and its members regularly visit the commercial galleries, meet collectors, organize lecture-demonstrations for students, and make trips to important exhibitions in Montreal, Ottawa, New York and Buffalo.

The collecting activity continues in conjunction with all these events, and every purchase is open to debate by young men who are learning about the national and international art scene. The committee recognizes that its work is no substitute for a University of Toronto collection, or for a multi-media academic programme in the visual arts. Those responsibilities remain a challenge which the university must meet. I cannot predict what the university will do to exploit the resources of our electronic, audio-visual age, but I am confident that the young people at Hart House will continue to experiment with new ideas and new programmes; indeed they may foster in the university a modernity that is beyond the philosophy of their academic mentors in the humanities. For Hart House is a self-renewing club; a New World club; a forum beyond Oxbridge in which young people can find creative opportunities to express their commitment to the variegated life of today.

This new catalogue of the Hart House collection is a gauge of what has been accomplished – and that is a great deal. But what, I wonder, will the next catalogue be like? Will it consist of slides or films? Will it record passing "environments" in the inner courtyard of Hart House (now used as a formal sculpture garden)? Will it show us images projected on the vaulted ceilings of Gothic corridors? Certainly Hart House and its art committee have moved beyond traditional ideas of what both a "club" and an "art collection" mean. The art committee originated in an *avant garde* atmosphere, and it shows every sign of continuing in this tradition. A century ago Baudelaire expressed the shock and delight of such a situation in one sentence: "For a long time I lived opposite a bar crudely striped in red and green; it gave my eyes delicious pain." This is the mode of youth. This is the mode of discovery and life.

Acknowledgements

E. A. WILKINSON
Warden

It was not by chance that the principal Founder of Hart House, the late Vincent Massey, included a reference to pictures in the prayer for the future institution. It was his hope that paintings and drawings would hang on the walls of our common rooms. In this way the members would become accustomed to art as they moved about their "house" and consciously or unconsciously would develop an interest in it. To the Right Honourable Vincent Massey, CC, CH, then, we make our first acknowledgement. He pointed the way.

The first funds were set aside for purchasing pictures during the wardenship of Walter Bowles, not long after the House opened its doors half a century ago. Collecting did not begin, however, until Burgon Bickersteth became Warden in 1921. He shared Mr. Massey's interest in paintings and fully realized the influence they might have on the lives of young men using the House, many of whom would thus be exposed to contemporary Canadian art for the first time. And so it is not surprising that the Hart House collection was started soon after he arrived, nor that it grew steadily in spite of the meagre funds available. It was during the Bickersteth years, beginning in 1922 with the purchase of A. Y. Jackson's *Georgian Bay, November*, that the House acquired some of its most important canvases.

To Nicholas Ignatieff and Joseph McCulley, who succeeded Mr. Bickersteth, we owe a great debt for their contribution to the further building of the collection. Nor must we ever forget the tremendously important rôle of the successive art committees of Hart House. In the final analysis it is these committees – composed of undergraduates, graduates and faculty – that have really made this fine collection. In the early days there was a formal advisory group of experts to guide them. Today the committee seeks assistance from a great variety of persons; artists, gallery directors, private collectors, and critics. No committee of the House works harder or takes its responsibilities more seriously. Its job has not been easy and grows increasingly difficult. Plagued by lack of funds and rising prices, the committees remain ever mindful of the need to keep standards high, of never buying just to add to the collection. The rewards are great – personally as well as to the House. Many readers of this book will be able to look back with justifiable pride and say, "That picture was purchased the year I was on the committee!"

I would like to acknowledge the work of certain individuals in connection with this book. Robert Hubbard, of the National Gallery of Canada, served as chairman of the editorial committee. Alan Toff was undergraduate secretary of Hart House during the planning and organization of contents. Jeremy Adamson, a former committee member and Keeper of the Prints, was editor, and prepared the catalogue while a student trainee at the National Gallery of Canada during 1967–8. Hugo McPherson was chairman of the committee when the printing of this catalogue was first proposed.

Finally, I wish to acknowledge the financial support of the Canada Council, the Province of Ontario Centennial Commission, the Varsity Fund, and the University of Toronto Press. Without their generous assistance the publication of this book would have been impossible.

Building the Hart House Collection

JEREMY ADAMSON

Today's undergraduate would find it extremely difficult to visualize the interior of Hart House without its collection of Canadian art. Paintings, prints and drawings are displayed on every available wall in almost every room used by the members of the House and its staff, and it often comes as a surprise to the visitor or the freshman student to recognize so many important and well-known canvases hanging in the common rooms. Hart House is a unique institution. It is essentially a private men's club, though membership is accorded automatically to all male students of the University of Toronto and is open to all male faculty members and graduates of the university. The magnificent neo-Gothic structure on the main campus is their athletic, social and cultural centre. It it also an educational centre, where, as is written in the Founders' Prayer, "the true education that is to be found in good fellowship, in friendly disputation and debate, in the conversation of wise and earnest men, in music, pictures and the play, in the casual book, in sports and games ..." takes place in friendly and informal surroundings.

A gift of the Massey Foundation, Hart House was opened in 1919. For fifty years it has provided a focus for the activities of thousands of undergraduates regardless of college or faculty affiliations. Its internal activities are organized and run by standing committees on which students, elected annually by the student membership, hold the majority. It is through this direct student participation that the domination of the House by its members is ensured. There is no immovable administrative hierarchy which so often alienates the student within the university structure, and though it may be physically imposing, Hart House is a personal and spontaneous place offering many different attractions to many different people. Long after their student years have passed, many graduates and professors retain senior memberships in this unusual club and serve with undergraduates on its committees.

The collection of Canadian paintings has grown with equal spontaneity. The House is not an art gallery, but it is filled with paintings; there is no professional curator, yet the collection is of national importance. Works are displayed throughout the House in such a way as to be readily accessible to the members. A museum atmosphere has been carefully avoided in favour of retaining the relaxed and immediate character of a collection hung in a private home. There is no attempt to organize the works into sequence or "schools"; instead pictures are rotated throughout the rooms during the academic year in order to give maximum exposure to the collection.

Considering the continual change in art committee membership over the past forty-odd years, it is surprising to find no serious lack of continuity in the calibre of the collection, and it is a tribute to successive generations of committee members that they have never strayed far from the original perceptive commitment to Canadian art. The collection, however, is not without its faults. Serious gaps exist. There are no canvases by Borduas or Riopelle, nor is the representation of the Regina School adequate. But these gaps, and the few mistakes in judgement which have been made, are more than compensated for by such triumphs of selection as Tom Thomson's *The Pointers*, Arthur Lismer's *Isles of Spruce*, Charles Comfort's *Young Canadian*, and Guido Molinari's *Espace jaune*, to name but a few. It is difficult, if not impossible, for even the most sophisticated collector – let alone an undergraduate committee member – continually to assess the spectrum of contemporary art and add important works to his collection every year. But this is what the Hart House art committee has always tried to do. It has the perennial challenge and responsibility to keep attuned to new directions in painting, printmaking and mixed media. To avoid the creative frontiers of the visual arts and to purchase works primarily because they fit into, or relate to, the existing collection would be the easy way out and the end of the importance of the Hart House collection; for such a conservative policy – eschewing the experimental and radical in contemporary art – would necessitate the purchase of outdated and mediocre works.

The genesis of its art activities began before Hart House was open to its members. On 17 January 1917, a notice was published in *The Varsity*:

All men of the University ... who are interested in Graphic Arts are invited to meet and form a new organization. Those who have a taste for drawing, painting or etching, or for art in general should find it of mutual advantage to have an organization.

The editors of the student newspaper had their comments on this proposal:

All that is needed is a centre to attract these men to each other. A place where they may work together. A place about a fire, with a circle of chairs, where over the smoke of black pipes and cigarettes the embryo Leonardos may air their views on Cubism, Futurism or any other "ism" not yet come to light; a place where the sketches of members could be hung for mutual criticism and advice from Canadian artists.

That same day after reading the notice in *The Varsity*, Vincent Massey, then involved in wartime military instruction, wrote to Joseph Banigan, a student in the Department of Architecture, that if such a club were formed and approved of by the university authorities it could easily be provided with quarters in Hart House, which was then under construction. About thirty men attended the first meeting, and having elected an executive they drew up a constitution. C. W. Jefferys, the well known historical illustrator and painter – then in charge of instruction in free-hand drawing and water colour painting at the university – pleaded that the organization be made a "working" club, pointing out the appalling lack of cartooning and illustration in *The Varsity* and *Torontonensis*. His advice was accepted. The purpose of the University of Toronto Sketch Club, as stated in its constitution, was "to encourage the practice and study of Fine Art, particularly the Graphic Arts, in the University of Toronto." The first world war, however, took its toll of student time and the club remained inactive until 1920. That year ties with Hart House were cemented. At a reorganization meeting in March it was proposed that the name be changed to the Hart House Sketch Club and that the room provided for its activities in the House – the present Art Gallery – be named the Sketch Room. Shortly afterwards, the Board of Stewards – the governing body of Hart House – adopted the club, the executive of which became one of the Board's standing committees. The activities of the club were then opened to the entire membership of the House.

The concept of art instruction was integral to the early development of the committee. Informal classes in elementary drawing and painting were held weekly in the Sketch Room, and such artists as C. W. Jefferys, F. S. Haines, Arthur Lismer and F. H. Varley were among the early instructors. In 1934, with the encouragement of Warden J. Burgon Bickersteth, an Arts and Crafts Room was set up next to the Camera Club's workroom. Here those interested in creating and printing woodcuts and etchings, metal working and wood carving could practise under Carl Schaefer. The work of the art class was regularly exhibited with that of other members of the House in the annual Members' Show held in the Art Gallery in the spring. Another creative effort sponsored by early committees was an annual competition for the university Christmas card: the winning student was awarded $25 and the University of Toronto Press printed the cards for sale to students and staff. University organizations also commissioned art committee and art class members to make their posters, and it was not long before the art life of Hart House was being strongly felt outside the House itself. In 1940 the arts and crafts instruction was discontinued owing to a lack of interest brought on by increasing military obligations on campus. Several postwar attempts were unsuccessfully made to rekindle interest but finally in 1948 the Arts and Crafts Room was given to the Camera Club. The drawing and painting classes are still very popular. Held twice a week on a shift basis, they provide rudimentary instruction from still life and models.

The "place about a fire" (the present Art Gallery) referred to in the 1917 *Varsity* article was both a workroom for the art classes, and a gallery for displaying works by members or professional artists. As the activities of the sketch committee grew – it was not until 1938 that the name *art* committee was adopted – additional space was acquired by annexing the old tuck shop and remodelling it into the present Print Room. A proper discussion of the exhibition programs carried out by the committee would necessitate a separate chapter. Sometimes dull and mediocre, sometimes extremely controversial and sometimes of great importance, these exhibitions have always complemented the permanent collection. Approximately ten exhibitions are organized each year for the following year, and except for a period in the summer the art gallery is continuously filled with paintings, graphics, sculpture or photographs. For many of the members these exhibitions are their first real contact with art. The exhibition policy has always been essentially unrestrictive, though it has been a general rule that Canadian works are usually shown, in part by unstated policy, in part because of the expense of shipping canvases or sculptures from the United States or from abroad. Consequently the art committee is free to choose works of men and women whose reputations have yet to be made, and there are many artists whose names are household words today who exhibited publicly for the first time in the Hart House gallery.

At an early point a collection of prints and reproductions was carefully assembled with the guidance of interested museum people to help create the material for an informal education in art history. The Keeper of the Prints, as that executive member of the committee appointed to care for this collection was rather grandly called, organized and mounted displays of a more didactic and historical nature in some of the common rooms and later in the Print Room. One such exhibition was entitled "The History of Western Painting; from Giotto to the Present" and ran in installments throughout an academic year. During the fifties these historical displays were supplanted by exhibitions of contemporary Canadian graphics. That thirty of these print exhibitions were mounted in the Print Room between 1953 and 1957 attests to the success of the committee in this venture.

In addition to the reproductions, the early committees began to assemble an art library. Its bookshelves, situated in one of the alcoves in the gallery, contain an interesting and varied selection of volumes on art history and techniques as well as exhibition catalogues and periodicals. Lectures on art appreciation and technique were often given to members of Hart House by the art class instructors or often by visiting artists and museum personnel. During the twenties and thirties, regular visits were arranged for committee members to the Royal Ontario Museum and the Art Gallery of Toronto to preview exhibitions, and to the studios of Toronto artists.

From the beginning a permanent collection was envisaged, and in 1925 the committee stated that it was "the policy of Hart House to form a collection of pictures representative of the best in Canadian art." To ensure that this policy was effectively carried out, an advisory board was set up composed of three artists or men especially interested in art nominated by the chairman of the committee. The original advisers were Lawren Harris, A. J. Casson and Gustav Hahn. In view of the situation at the time this was a necessary procedure. Few commercial galleries in Toronto showed contemporary art. Some was hung at the annual group exhibitions at the Art Gallery of Toronto – those of the Royal Canadian Academy and Ontario Society of Artists, for example – but the nature of such societies is to eschew the controversial and up-to-date, and the competition among collectors for what was shown there was fierce. Consequently these exhibitions could not be counted on as a major source of purchases. The advisers to the art committee, as artists themselves, would in the course of visits to friends' studios become aware of important canvases being executed and of others still in the artists' possession. These they could secure for the committee to choose from. At this early point there were two directions open to the House. One was to follow the accepted taste of the day and select safe, academic landscapes, still lifes and portraits; the other was to branch out and form a collection of *avant garde* works. Fortunately for us today, the committee chose the latter.

The first painting in the collection, purchased by the art committee of 1921–2, was A. Y. Jackson's *Georgian Bay, November*. It became the cornerstone of the collection only two years after the formation of the Group of Seven painters, and for that time it was a radical choice. Though the criticism levelled at the Group was waning by 1922 – the press had earlier likened their paintings to "Hungarian goulash" and "the contents of a drunkard's stomach" – their work was still considered highly suspect. Now committed to the *avant garde* movement, the committee went on to purchase other and major canvases by the Group of Seven. It is interesting to note that nearly all were bought during the Group's "classical" period before they disbanded in 1933.

The moving force behind the art committee in these early days was its first chairman, Professor Barker Fairley of the German Department, University College. It was through his friendship with the Group of Seven and other contemporary artists that Hart House became closely linked with the national movement, and it was he who wisely solicited the help of the early advisers. They and their successors appear to have taken their responsibilities seriously, ferreting out canvases which otherwise might not have come to the notice of the committee. Important works which entered the collection in the late twenties and early thirties included Edwin Holgate's *Fire Ranger* (acquired in 1926), Arthur Lismer's *Isles of Spruce* (1927), Tom Thomson's *The Pointers* (1928), Emily Carr's *Kitwancool Totems* (1929), A. Y. Jackson's *October Morning, Algoma* (1931), Lawren Harris's *Red House* (1932), J. E. H. MacDonald's *October Shower Gleam* (1933), and Charles Comfort's *Young Canadian* (1934). During the early years when the collection was small, the artists who lent paintings to the annual September exhibition of Canadian painting were asked to continue the loan during the winter months and thus augment the works owned by the House. There was also a reciprocal agreement with art galleries which borrowed Hart House paintings for exhibitions of their own, whereby they lent other pictures to cover the gaps left in the collection. By 1935, however, the Hart House collection was large enough that it was no longer necessary to borrow paintings to keep the common rooms from looking barren.

The fact that many of the early acquisitions were borrowed for major exhibitions of Canadian art in London, Paris, New York, San Francisco and Washington – beginning with the now famous showings of Canadian painting at the British Empire Exhibition at Wembley in 1924 and 1925 – attests to the importance they were accorded and to the early international renown of the Hart House collection. In 1938, when the number of works owned by the House was fewer than fifty, eleven canvases were lent to "A Century of Canadian Art", an exhibition organized by the National Gallery of Canada and held at the Tate Gallery, London.

The funds for purchase originally came from two main sources: the proceeds of the house committee's popular Masquerade Ball, held annually during the 1920s and 1930s, and donations by the students of the graduating year. Evidently the ball was regularly a great success (except for a period during the darkest years of the Depression), for a large number of paintings were acquired through it; they are marked "Purchased by the House Committee" in the catalogue entries. Though the response from the graduating students was less reliable, in general the early art committee could count on making two purchases a year. Today the committee has its own budget, allocated by the Board of Stewards from the annual membership fees. The number of canvases which enter the collection each year varies. Often as many as five purchases have been made, and there have been years when no suitable painting could be recommended. Student groups still take an interest, often donating money for a purchase to be made in their name. Funds are also available from the accrued income of an endowment established in 1927 by Professor George Wrong in memory of his sons Harold and Murray, and there are occasional contributions from the Varsity Fund and various alumni groups. The Warden has, on several occasions, made eleventh-hour monies available to the art committee for major purchases. As a general rule gifts of paintings are not accepted, although important canvases have been acquired in this way, including the two Krieghoff paintings and David Milne's *Water Lilies, Temagami*.

A major, though short-lived addition was made during the second world war when Lord and Lady Lee of Fareham gave their valuable collection of mediaeval and Renaissance *objets d'art* to the Massey Foundation for safe-keeping in Canada. The Lee

Collection was housed in a special display area at the west end of the Reading Room from 1948 until 1960, when it was transferred to the Royal Ontario Museum where, on indefinite loan, it is a major attraction.

In the winter of 1944 the art committee organized an exhibition of paintings by the Montreal artist Jacques de Tonnancour. It was the first exhibition of work by a French-Canadian artist to be shown in the Hart House gallery and from it the committee purchased *The Blue Dress*, thus establishing its first link with the vital artistic awakening among Quebec artists. Up to this point Canadian painting, especially in English-speaking Canada, revolved around Group of Seven-influenced landscapes and relatively unimaginative portraiture. Although Hart House had made some excellent figurative purchases, such as Comfort's *Young Canadian* and Jack Humphrey's *Draped Head*, the collection was plainly dominated by the popular aesthetic of the Group of Seven. Another link with the new French-Canadian art was made with the 1947 purchase of Goodridge Roberts' *Portrait of a Girl*, but canvases by Pellan, Borduas and Riopelle, whose inspiration was Paris Surrealism, were unfortunately missed. This was primarily due to the lack of awareness on the part of Toronto dealers and collectors at large of the artistic revolution that was taking place in Montreal and Quebec. Unfortunately these gaps are unlikely to be filled. With its limited budget the committee cannot purchase works which have passed the test of time, for in passing such a test they have also passed out of the range of available funds. Thanks, however, to generosity of a great friend, Mr. Charles McFaddin, registrar of the Art Gallery of Ontario, an early Pellan painting entered the collection in 1964.

If Montreal artists looked to Paris in the 1940s, Toronto painters were attracted to the Abstract Expressionist painters of New York. Under the leadership of Jock Macdonald, who was a most influential teacher at the Ontario College of Art by the late forties, several of his pupils began to develop along radical lines. With several other sympathetic artists, they formed the group "Painters Eleven" and exhibited their work to the shock of the Toronto public. Their first exhibition alienated the established art interests. There were few galleries in Ontario which would exhibit their work – the one early exception in Toronto being the Hart House gallery.

By the advent of the 1950s non-objective and abstract compositions had become part of the language of artists in Toronto, and controversy broke out between non-objective and representational factions. This new aesthetic became a problem to the art committee. In the annual report for 1949–50, the secretary of the committee (an undergraduate) noted

> a falling off in interest of the men of Hart House in art ... This loss of interest is most plainly explained by the widening breach between artists and their public. The percentage of abstract and non-objective art is rising with a consequent growth in public apathy.

Hart House was not, however, entirely devoid of abstract painting in 1950. Lawren Harris had given the House a fine example of his non-objective work in 1949, and the collection included a small canvas and a water colour by Bertram Brooker as well as Fritz Brandtner's *Lost City*.

The art committee, while not reactionary, found, like many organizations and people, the change in language in the visual arts a difficult period of adjustment. A few works of questionable value were purchased: many contemporary artists in Canada were undergoing a period of intense experimentation and self-examination and the results were often unsuccessful. A special committee composed of Barker Fairley, Aba Bayefsky and W. S. A. Dale was formed in 1958 to assess the quality of the permanent collection as a whole. Their report, not as optimistic as might have been hoped, stated in part:

The committee feels that greater care should be taken in the selection of purchases. Hart House has a national reputation to keep up. The merely fashionable and commercially successful should be avoided in favour of the genuinely original, and the chief criteria should be the quality of the individual work of art.

Although such a statement oversimplifies the matter, it underscores the essential responsibility of the art committee – and of any purchasing committee – to refresh itself continually, to detach its perceptions from the existing collection, and to buy each painting as though it were the first to be acquired. It is easy to become complacent, selecting pieces which fit into the collection without disturbing the equilibrium, rather than searching out elusive but important additions. The purchase of A. Y. Jackson's *Georgian Bay, November* in 1922 hardly seems radical and daring today, but the first Group of Seven exhibition in 1920 shocked the Toronto public profoundly, perhaps more than the first Painters Eleven exhibition did thirty-four years later. The art committee supported the Group of Seven early in their careers, to the chagrin of some members of the University community, but this support has paid aesthetic dividends far in excess of what the original committee might have imagined. Since the early 1960s the Hart House collection has expanded rapidly, and paintings truly representative of contemporary art in Canada have appeared on the common room walls. The purchase in 1961 of Harold Town's *Homage to Turner* and Jock Macdonald's *Airy Journey* provided the necessary breakthrough. The Town canvas met strong resistance at first, but with the energetic and often controversial exhibitions in the art gallery and the more recent purchases of Yves Gaucher's *Signals No. 4* and Mashel Teitelbaum's *Heraldic Gold*, undergraduates are becoming well acquainted with the wide range and rich vitality of painting and printmaking in Canada today.

Aside from a few minor exhibition programs – though certainly of value in themselves – initiated by individual colleges, there is no concerted effort on the part of the university as a whole to inform its students about art in general, and in particular about the visual arts in Canada. The academic aspects of art history are dealt with by the Department of Fine Art, but for the student of engineering or psychology Hart House remains the sole link with our artistic heritage, past and present. As the University of Toronto continues to grow in size and complexity, so must the art activities of Hart House if the House is to maintain its unique and leading role within the university in the sphere of informal education and activity outside the lecture room or laboratory. A point in time has been reached when the House must decide on either an isolationist or expansionist policy, either remaining satisfied with the limited exhibition, storage and display space for the collection, or undertaking to press for a new art gallery and an expanded exhibition program. Already the existing wall space, which up to now has been adequate to display the entire collection, is almost exhausted. Perhaps too it is a time when certain unobtrusive aspects of a museum environment could be instituted, without eliminating the relaxed and accessible atmosphere which characterizes the common rooms, in order to ensure the preservation of the paintings for future generations of undergraduates.

It has been said that the art gallery should play a subversive role within the community, upsetting applecarts and expanding perceptions in order that we may learn to see the reality of our physical environment. In a university community this is doubly necessary, for one generation of students is likely to be the next generation's arbiters of taste. If Hart House is to rise to the challenge, it must continue to show its committed and responsive attitude toward changing needs and demands and play an increasingly important educational role within the University of Toronto.

THE HART HOUSE COLLECTION OF CANADIAN PAINTINGS

140 TOM THOMSON *Birches*

61 CORNELIUS KRIEGHOFF *Coureur de bois*

8 FREDERICK BELL-SMITH
Mist, Rocky Mountains

141 TOM THOMSON *The Pointers*

7 J. W. BEATTY *Beech Tree*

152 F. H. VARLEY *Vincent Massey*

150 F. H. VARLEY *Magic Tree*

58 A. Y. JACKSON *October Morning, Algoma*

75 J. E. H. MACDONALD *Laurentian Village*

21 EMILY CARR *Kitwancool Totems*

52 EDWIN HOLGATE *Fire Ranger*

94 JAMES WILSON MORRICE
Algiers

57 A. Y. JACKSON *Labrador Coast*

119 W. J. PHILLIPS
York Boat on Lake Winnipeg

66 ARTHUR LISMER *Isles of Spruce*

20 FRANK CARMICHAEL *Snow Clouds*

15 F. H. BRIGDEN *Summer Morning in the Valley*

155 F. H. VARLEY *Open Window*

35 L. L. FITZGERALD *Summer*

76 J. E. H. MACDONALD *October Shower Gleam*

55 JACK HUMPHREY *Draped Head*

83 DAVID MILNE *Water Lilies, Temagami*

49 LAWREN HARRIS *Red House, Winter*

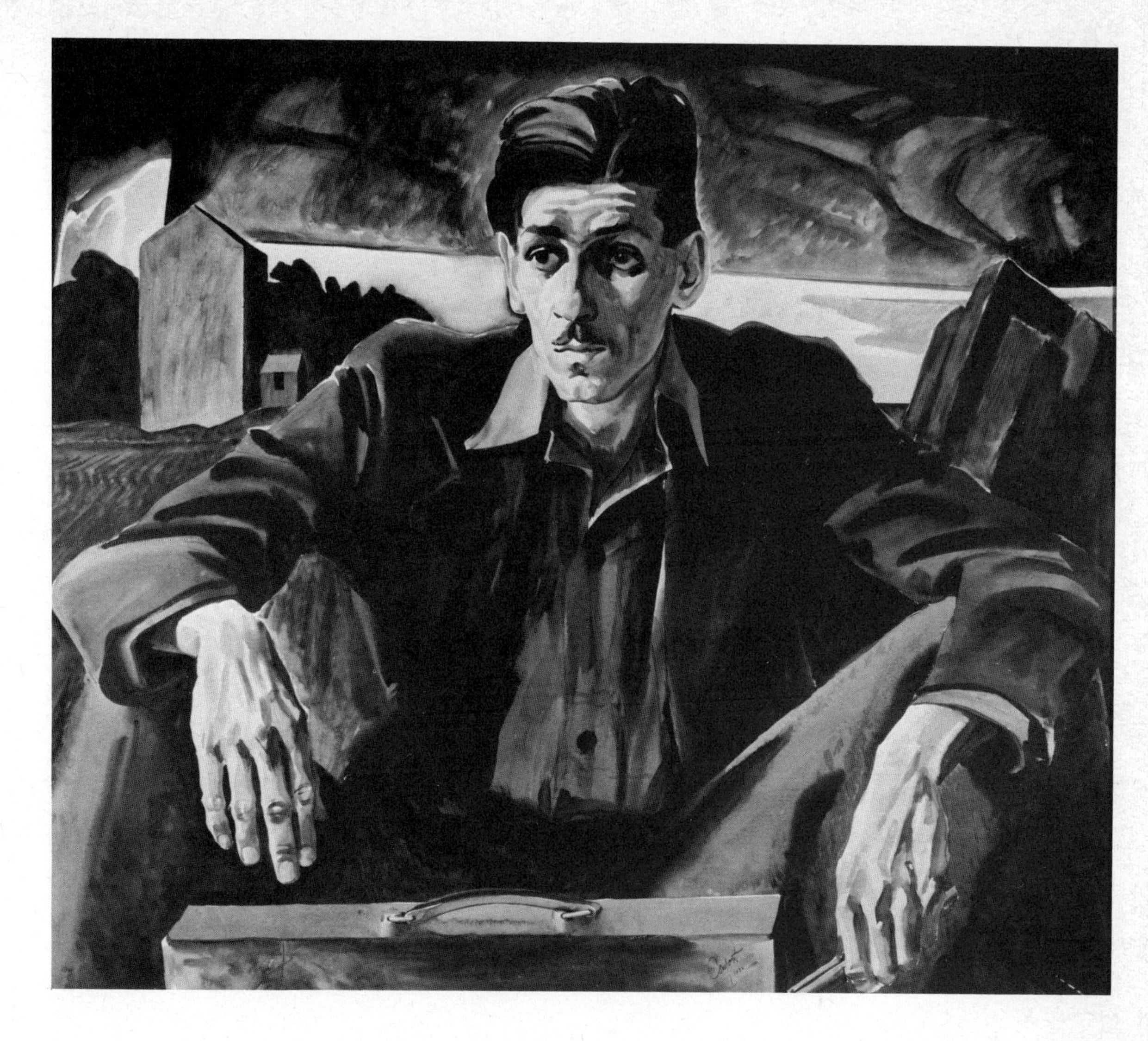

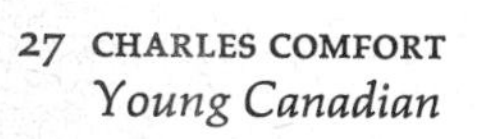

27 CHARLES COMFORT
Young Canadian

45 LAWREN HARRIS *Islands, Lake Superior*

53 YVONNE HOUSSER
South Shore, Quebec

46 LAWREN HARRIS
Isolation Peak

22 A. J. CASSON *Golden October*

56 A. Y. JACKSON *Georgian Bay, November*

51 PRUDENCE HEWARD *Dark Girl*

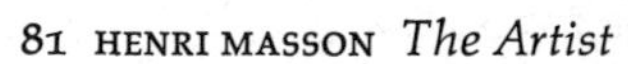

81 HENRI MASSON *The Artist*

101 LILIAS TORRANCE NEWTON *Maurice*

107 WILL OGILVIE *Hart House Chapel Murals* (detail)

54 E. J. HUGHES *Qualicum Beach*

124 GOODRIDGE ROBERTS *Portrait of a Girl*

24 PARASKEVA CLARK *In the Woods*

153 F. H. VARLEY *Self Portrait*

85 DAVID MILNE *Scaffolding*

10 B. C. BINNING *Small Boats Frolicking near a Blue Diving Tower*

144 JACQUES DE TONNANCOUR *The Blue Dress*

29 STANLEY COSGROVE *Still Life*

77 JOCK MACDONALD *Airy Journey*

113 ALFRED PELLAN *La fenêtre ouverte*

18 BERTRAM BROOKER *Leaf Sonata*

158 SYDNEY WATSON
City, Back Elevation

73 GRANT MACDONALD *Girl in White*

44 LAWREN HARRIS *Abstract*

93 GUIDO MOLINARI *Espace jaune*

3 ABA BAYEFSKY *Market Forms*

133 GORDON A. SMITH *Rocks with Yellow*

30 GRAHAM COUGHTRY
Two Figure Series, No. 10

111 L. A. C. PANTON *Untitled*

145 **HAROLD TOWN**
Homage to Turner

104 JACK NICHOLS *Pierrot with Ball*

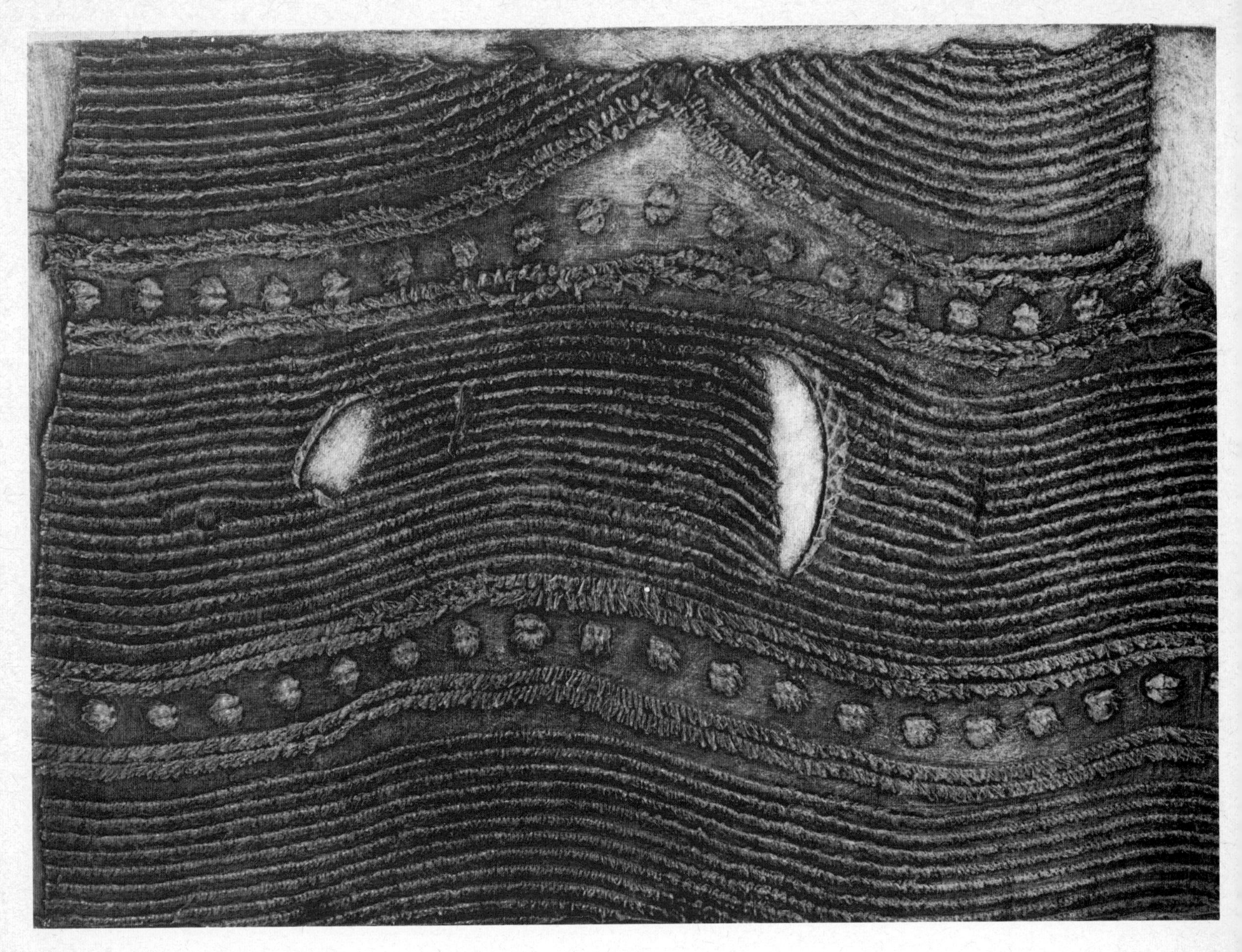

31 ALBERT DUMOUCHEL *Premier labour*

96 NORVAL MORRISEAU
Fish Cycle

39 LISE GERVAIS *Nous n'irons plus au bois*

130 JACK SHADBOLT
Northern Elegy No. 2

139 MASHEL TEITELBAUM *Heraldic Gold*

64 JEAN-PAUL LEMIEUX *La chandaille rouge*

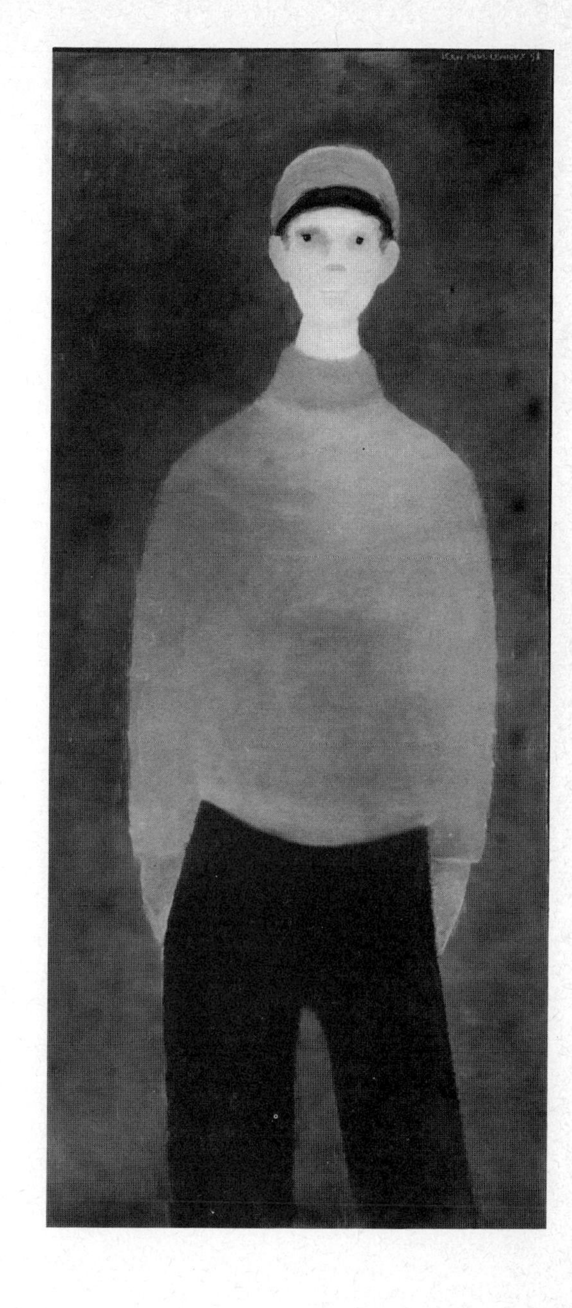

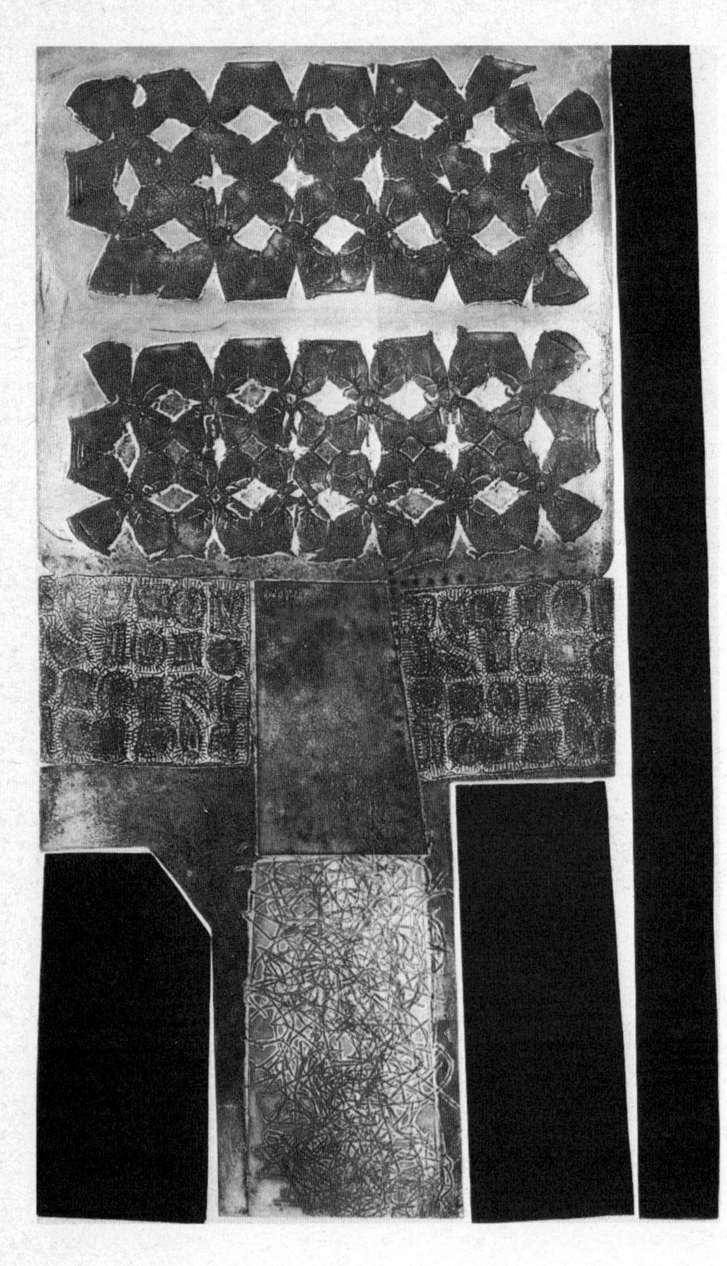

33 JOHN ESLER *Freeway and the Cherry Orchard, No. 1*

126 BENITA SANDERS *Ziggurat*

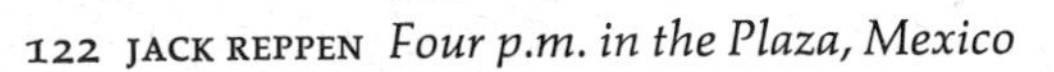

122 JACK REPPEN *Four p.m. in the Plaza, Mexico*

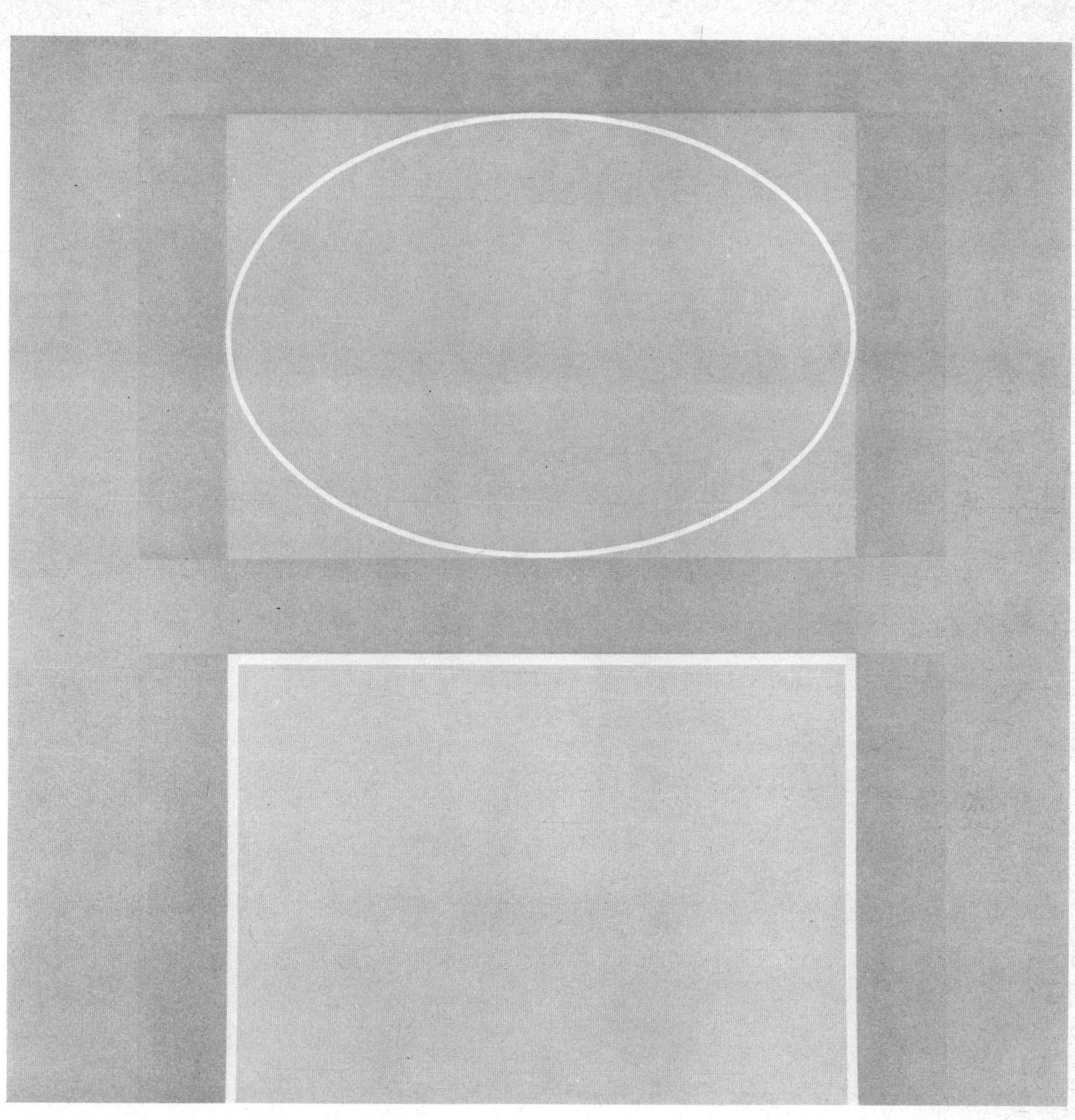

60 ROY KIYOOKA *The Ring and the Window*

65 LES LEVINE *Drawing IV*

80 JEAN MCEWEN *La victoire de Sardanapale*

1

2

4

All measurements are given with the vertical first
Paintings marked with an asterisk are not reproduced
Abbreviations are explained on page 112

BANTING, SIR FREDERICK G. (1891–1941)

1
Elora (1927)
oil on panel
8½ x 10½
Gift of A. Y. Jackson, 1962
Literature
A. Y. Jackson, *Banting as an Artist* (1943), p. 35, repr. p. 30
Exhibitions
Hart House, *Sir Frederick Banting*, 1943

2
French Countryside (1937)
oil on canvas
8½ x 10½
Gift of Lady Banting
Literature
A. Y. Jackson, *Banting as an Artist* (1943), p. 32
Exhibitions
Hart House, *Sir Frederick Banting*, 1943

BAYEFSKY, ABA (1925–)

3
Market Forms
oil on canvas
38 x 51
signed and dated upper left: AB/56
Purchased by the Graduate Committee of Hart House and the Engineering Society, 1956

4
Boy with Butterflies (1948)
conté crayon
15½ x 19½
Purchased by the Art Committee 1949–50
Literature
Harper (1955), p. 74
Exhibitions
Toronto, AGT, 1950, No. 303

5
D.P. Children (1948)
pastel with pen and ink
11 x 15½
Purchased by the Art Committee, 1949–50

6
D.P. Mother Feeding Child (1948)
pen and ink
11 x 16
Purchased by the Art Committee, 1949–50
Literature
Harper (1955), p. 74

BEATTY, J. W. (1868–1941)

7
Beech Tree (also known as *Forest Interior, Edge of the Woods* and *Beechwood*) (1916)
oil on canvas
25 x 40
signed lower left: J. W. BEATTY
Gift of the Graduating Year of 1924

Literature

D. Buchanan, *Canadian Painters* (1945), pl. 28
D. Hoover, *J. W. Beatty* (1948), p. 26
Harper (1955), p. 9

Exhibitions

Toronto, CNE, 1917, No. 119 (illus. p. 48)
Toronto, OSA, 1917, No. 5 (illus.)
Winnipeg, WAG, 1921, No. 21 (illus. p. 17)
London, Tate, 1938, No. 5

BELL-SMITH, FREDERICK M. (1846–1923)

8
Mist, Rocky Mountains
water colour
13 x 18
signed and dated lower right: *F. M. Bell-Smith 1890*
Purchased by the Art Committee, 1935

Literature

Harper (1955), p. 6

Exhibitions

London, Tate, 1938, No. 8

BIELER, ANDRÉ (1896–)

9
The Saw Mill (1933)
caseine on canvas
19 x 23
signed lower right: AB
Gift of the Graduating Year of 1938

Literature

Harper (1955), p. 52

Exhibitions

Toronto, AGT, *CGP*, 1936, No. 1d
London, Tate, 1938, No. 10

5

6

9

11

12

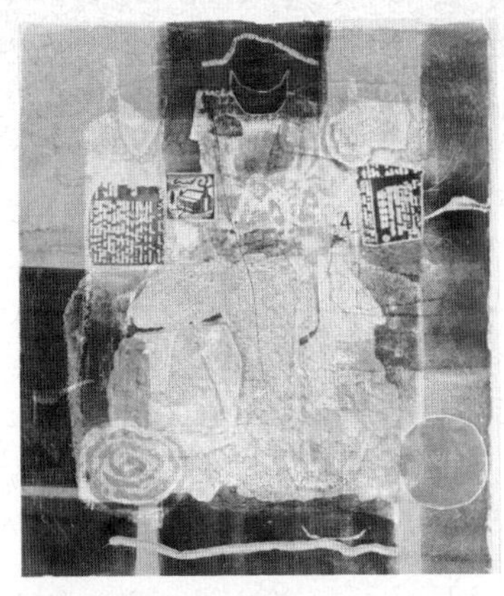

13

14

BINNING, BERTRAM C. (1909–)

10
Small Boats Frolicking near a Blue Diving Tower
oil on canvas
19 x 29½
signed and dated lower centre
B. C. Binning '49
Purchased by the Art Committee, 1949–50
Literature
Harper (1955), p. 73
Exhibitions
Boston, 1949, No. 3
Reproduced
CA, vol. vi, 1949, p. 150

BOBAK, BRUNO (1925–)

11
Cross Country Convoy
water colour
12 x 22
signed and dated lower left:
BOBAK, *1943*
Purchased by the Art Committee, 1944
Exhibitions
Ottawa, NGC, *Canadian Army Art Exhibition*, 1944
(awarded First Prize)
Reproduced
CA, vol. 1, 1944, p. 135

BOUCHARD, SIMONE MARY (1912–45)

12
Nature Morte Antique 1942
oil on silk
21 x 12
signed lower left:
S. Mary Bouchard
Purchased by the Art Committee, 1942

BOYD, JAMES HENDERSON (1928–)

13
Un Bon Vivant
relief print
16 x 12 (sight)
signed lower right:
James Boyd
dated lower left: */63*
Purchased by the Art Committee, 1964–5

BRANDTNER, FRITZ (1896–)

14
Lost City (ca. 1945)
water colour
14½ x 11½
Purchased by the Art Committee, 1949–50
Literature
Harper (1955), p. 76
Exhibitions
Toronto, AGT, 1950, No. 168

BRIGDEN, FREDERICK H.
(1871–1956)

15
Summer Morning in the Valley
oil on canvas
36 x 42
signed and dated lower right:
F. H. BRIGDEN *32*
Purchased by the House Committee, 1932–3
Literature
Harper (1955), p. 12
Exhibitions
Toronto, CNE, 1932, No. 89 (illus. p. 30)
Toronto, CNE, 1950, No. 3

16
Okanagan Country (1942)
water colour
10 x 14
signed lower right:
F. H. BRIGDEN
Purchased by the House Committee, 1944–5

BROOKER, BERTRAM (1888–1955)

17
Wings and Waves (1949)
oil on composition board
11 x 14½
Purchased by the Art Committee, 1949–50
Literature
Harper (1955), p. 79

18
Leaf Sonata (also known as *Dahliana*) (1949)
water colour
10½ x 14½
Purchased by the Art Committee, 1949–50
Literature
Harper (1955), p. 79
Reproduced
Paul Duval, *Canadian Water-Colour Painting* (1954), p. 43

CAISERMAN-ROTH, GHITTA
(1923–)

19
Boy with Chicken
Lithograph
23 x 16
Purchased by the Art Committee, 1951–2

CARMICHAEL, FRANK
(1890–1945)

20
Snow Clouds
oil on canvas
40 x 48
signed and dated lower right:
FRANK CARMICHAEL *1926*
Gift of the Graduating Year of 1926
Literature
Housser (1926), p. 217
Harper (1955), p. 25
Exhibitions
Toronto, AGT, 1926, No. 2
Ottawa, NGC, 1927, No. 28
Ottawa, NGC, 1936, No. 3
London, Tate, 1938, No. 22
Vancouver, VAG, 1954, No. 1 (illus.)
Port Arthur, Lakehead College, 1964, No. 1

16

17

19

23

25

CARR, EMILY (1871–1945)

21
Kitwancool Totems
oil on canvas
42 x 27
signed and dated lower left:
M. EMILY CARR KITWACOOL *1928*
Gift of the Graduating Year
of 1929
Literature
B. Brooker, *Yearbook of the Arts in Canada* (1929), p. 288, pl. xi
Harper (1955), p. 49
Exhibitions
St. Louis, 1930, No. 7
Ottawa, NGC, *Emily Carr*, 1945, No. 26
New York, Canadian Club, 1948, No. 5 (illus. pl. 6)
Richmond, Va., 1949, No. 14

CASSON, ALFRED J. (1898–)

22
Golden October (also known as *Autumn Evening*) (1935)
oil on canvas
40 x 60
signed lower right: A. J. CASSON
Purchased with income from the Harold and Murray Wrong Memorial Fund, 1939
Literature
Paul Duval, *A. J. Casson* (1951) illus. p. 43
Harper (1955), p. 35
Exhibitions
Toronto, OSA, 1935, No. 26 (illus.)
Toronto, CNE, 1936, No. 227 (illus.)
?Toronto, OSA, 1939, No. 26
RCA, 1939, No. 39
Reproduced
CA, vol. XX, 1963, p. 218

23
Breezy Day (1927)
water colour
17 x 20
signed lower right: A. J. CASSON
Gift of the Graduating Year
of 1927
Literature
Harper (1955), p. 30

CLARK, PARASKEVA (1898–)

24
In the Woods (also known as *Forest Interior*)
oil on canvas
30 x 27
signed and dated lower right:
PARASKEVA CLARK *39*
Purchased with income from the Harold and Murray Wrong Memorial Fund, 1939
Literature
Harper (1955), p. 59
Exhibitions
New Haven, Yale University, 1944
Toronto, AGT, 1945, No. 192
Washington, 1950, No. 16 (illus.)
Reproduced
CA, vol. 5, 1947, p. 65
CA, vol. XVII, 1960, p. 292

COMFORT, CHARLES F. (1900–)

25
Prairie Road
oil on canvas
46 x 34
signed and dated lower right:
COMFORT *'25*
Gift of the Graduating Year
of 1931
Exhibitions
Ottawa, NGC, 1931, No. 48
Toronto, CNE, 1952, No. 65

26
Saguenay River (1935)
oil on canvas
30 x 36
Gift of the Graduating Year of 1935
Literature
Harper (1955), p. 54

27
Young Canadian
water colour
36 x 42
signed and dated lower right centre: COMFORT/*1932*
Purchased by the Sketch Committee, 1934
Literature
Buchanan (1950), p. 58, pl. 38
Paul Duval, *Canadian Water-Colour Painting* (1954), p. 39
Harper (1955), p. 53
Harper (1966), p. 335, pl. 307
Exhibitions
Toronto, CNE, 1934, No. 381 (illus. p. 65)
London, Tate, 1938, No. 39
New York, World's Fair, 1939, No. 30 (Canadian Section)
Andover, Mass., 1942, No. 26 (illus.)
Toronto, AGT, 1945, No. 167
New Haven, Yale University, 1944 (illus.)
Toronto, CNE, 1948, No. 89
Washington, 1950, No. 19 (illus.)
Mexico City, 1960, No. 138
Stratford, Ont., 1964
Vancouver, VAG, 1966, No. 91

COOMBS, E. GRACE (1890–)

28
Windswept Pines
oil on canvas
20 x 24
signed and dated lower right: E. GRACE COOMBS *1923*
Purchased by the House Committee, 1922–3
Literature
Lorne Pierce, *E. Grace Coombs* (1949), p. 7 (repr. in colour)
Harper (1955), p. 47
Exhibitions
Toronto, OSA, 1923, No. 30

COSGROVE, STANLEY (1911–)

29
Still Life
oil on composition board
20 x 22
signed and dated lower right: COSGROVE *47*
Gift of Mrs. H. A. Dyde in Memory of Alan Plaunt, University College, 1922
Literature
Harper (1955), p. 72

COUGHTRY, GRAHAM (1931–)

30
Two Figure Series, No. 10
oil and lucite on canvas
62 x 72
signed and dated lower right: COUGHTRY *63*
Purchased by the Art Committee, 1963–4

DUMOUCHEL, ALBERT (1911–)

31
Premier labour
relief print
18⅝ x 25¾
signed and dated lower right: ALBERT DUMOUCHEL *64*
Purchased by the Art Committee, 1964–5

26

28

32

34

36

37

ELIOT, RUTH M. (1913–)

32
Winter, Ottawa (1934)
oil on panel
16 x 11½
Purchased by the Sketch Committee, 1934

ESLER, JOHN K. (1933–)

33
Freeway and the Cherry Orchard, No. 1
relief print
36 x 21½
signed and dated lower right:
JOHN K. ESLER '65
Purchased by the Art Committee, 1966–7

FAIRLEY, BARKER (1887–)

34
Shirley (1938)
oil on canvas
13 x 11
Purchased by the Art Committee, 1955

FITZGERALD, LIONEL LEMOINE (1890–1956)

35
Summer (1931)
oil on cotton
14 x 17
signed lower left:
L. L. FITZGERALD
Gift of the Graduating Year of 1933
Literature
Harper (1955), p. 35
Exhibitions
Ottawa, NGC, 1936, No. 47
London, Tate, 1938, No. 53

36
Prairie Trail (1955)
pen and ink
10 x 15
signed lower left:
L. L. FITZGERALD
Gift of J. B. Bickersteth, 1955

GAUCHER, YVES (1933–)

37
Signals No. 4 (1966)
acrylic on canvas
48 x 60
Purchased by the Art Committee, 1966–7

38
Sono
relief impression on laminated paper
24⅛ x 35¾
signed and dated lower right:
GAUCHER *'63*
Purchased by the Art Committee, 1964–5

GERVAIS, LISE (1933–)

39
Nous n'irons plus au bois
oil on canvas
60 x 48
signed and dated lower right:
GERVAIS *65*
Purchased by the Art Committee, 1965–6

GILSON, JACQUELINE (1912–)

40
Red and Green
oil on canvas
37 x 60½
signed and dated upper right:
JACQUELINE GILSON *45*
Purchased by the Art Committee, 1951–2
Literature
Harper (1955), p. 70
Reproduced
Etienne Gilson, *Painting and Reality* (1955), pl. 56

GREENE, THOMAS G. (1875–1955)

41
Storm, Lake Simcoe (ca. 1926)
oil on canvas
24 x 30
signed lower right: T. G. GREENE
Purchased by the House Committee, 1926–7
Literature
Harper (1955), p. 46
Exhibitions
St. Louis, 1930, No. 15

HAINES, FREDERICK S. (1879–1960)

42
Poplars (1926)
oil on canvas
48 x 55
signed lower left: HAINES
Purchased by the House Committee, 1929–30
Literature
Harper (1955), p. 11
Exhibitions
Toronto, OSA, 1930, No. 68
London, Tate, 1938, No. 78

38

41

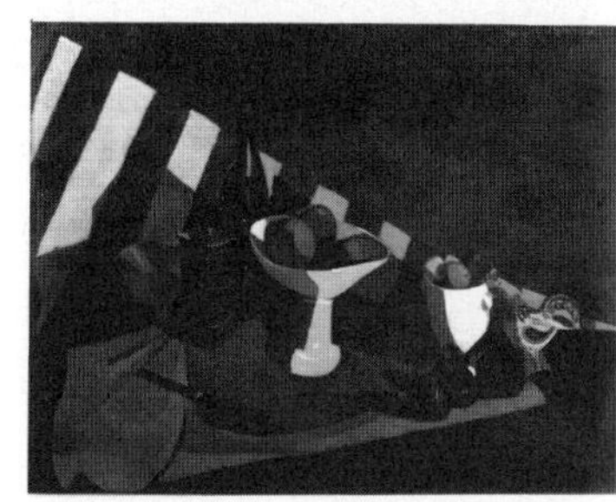

40

42

43

47

HARRIS, BESS (LARKIN) HOUSSER (1890–)

43
Laurentian Village (ca. 1930)
oil on canvas
36 x 45
signed lower right:
BESS HOUSSER
Gift of the House Committee, 1930–1
Exhibitions
St. Louis, 1930, No. 28 (illus.)

HARRIS, LAWREN S. (1885–)

44
Abstract (1943)
oil on canvas
42 x 30
Gift of the Artist, 1949
Literature
Harper (1955), p. 39
Harper (1966), p. 360, pl. 328
Exhibitions
Toronto, AGT, *Lawren Harris*, 1948, No. 58 (detail repr. on cover)
Ottawa, NGC, *Lawren Harris*, 1963, No. 51
Reproduced
CA, Apr.–May 1944, p.47
CA, vol. iv, 1947, p. 83

45
Islands, Lake Superior (1922)
oil on panel
11 x 14
signed lower right:
LAWREN HARRIS
Purchased by the House Committee, 1923–4
Literature
Harper (1955), p. 24

46
Isolation Peak (ca. 1931)
oil on canvas
42 x 50
Purchased with the income from the Harold and Murray Wrong Memorial Fund, 1946
Literature
Harper (1955), p. 34
Exhibitions
Ottawa, NGC, 1932, No. 98
?Rio de Janeiro, 1944, No. 81
Toronto, AGT, *Lawren Harris*, 1948, No. 53
Ottawa, NGC, *Lawren Harris* 1963, No. 37
Reproduced
Montreal Lithography Co., calendar illustration, 1966

47
Lake, Spruce and Mist (ca. 1920)
oil on panel
11 x 14
signed lower right:
LAWREN HARRIS
Purchased by the House Committee, 1923–4

48
Newfoundland Sketch (1921)
oil on panel
11 x 14
signed lower left:
LAWREN HARRIS
Purchased by the House Committee, 1923–4

49
Red House, Winter (ca. 1925)
oil on canvas
35 x 41
Gift of the Graduating Year of 1932
Literature
Harper (1955), p. 33 (repr. in colour)

HEDRICK, ROBERT (1930–)

50
Aquarium No. 1
brush and ink
39½ x 26½
signed and dated lower right:
HEDRICK/*63*
Purchased by the Art Committee, 1964–5

HEWARD, PRUDENCE
(1896–1965)

51
Dark Girl (1935–6)
oil on canvas
36 x 39
signed lower left: P. H.
Purchased with the income from the Harold and Murray Wrong Memorial Fund, 1936
Literature
Harper (1955), p. 55
Exhibitions
Toronto, AGT, *CGP*, 1936, No. 36 (illus.)
London, Tate, 1938, No. 96 (illus.)
Toronto, AGT, 1945, No. 170
Ottawa, NGC, *Prudence Heward*, 1948, No. 97
Hamilton, AGH, 1953, No. 21 (illus.)
Reproduced
B. Brooker, *Yearbook of the Arts in Canada* (1936), pl. 56

HOLGATE, EDWIN H. (1892–)

52
Fire Ranger (Garde forestier) (1926)
oil on canvas
22 x 18
signed lower left: E. HOLGATE
Purchased by the House Committee, 1925–6
Literature
Harper (1955), p. 32
Exhibitions
Philadelphia, 1926 (Canadian Section)
Ottawa, NGC, 1927, No. 102
St. Louis, 1930, No. 27
Ottawa, NGC, 1936, No. 94
Reproduced
CA, vol. V, 1947, p. 66

HOUSSER, YVONNE (MCKAGUE)
(1898–)

53
South Shore, Quebec (1933)
oil on canvas
24 x 30
signed lower left:
YVONNE MCKAGUE
Gift of the Graduating Year, 1934
Literature
Harper (1955), p. 51
Exhibitions
Toronto, OSA, 1934, No. 98 (illus. p. 6)

HUGHES, EDWARD J. (1913–)

54
Qualicum Beach
oil on canvas
36 x 42
signed and dated lower right:
E. J. HUGHES *1948*
Purchased by the Art Committee, 1949–50
Literature
Harper (1955), p. 80
Exhibitions
Vancouver, VAG, *E. J. Hughes*, 1967, No. 9 (repr. in colour on cover)
Reproduced
Artscanada, No. 115, Dec. 1967

48

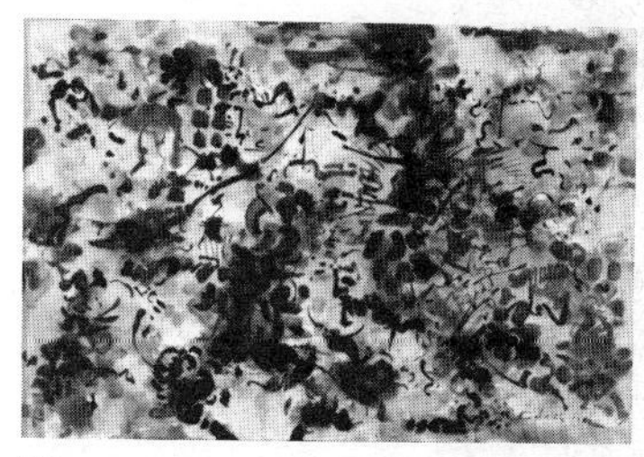
50

59

HUMPHREY, JACK W. (1901–67)

55
Draped Head (1931)
oil on paper panel
16 x 12
signed upper right:
Jack Humphrey
Gift of the Graduating Year of 1937
Literature
Harper (1955), p. 48
Harper (1966), p. 329
Exhibitions
Toronto, AGT, *CGP*, 1937, No. 93 (illus.)
Ottawa, NGC, *CGP*, 1938, No. 40
London, Tate, 1938, No. 108
Andover, Mass., 1942, No. 34
Ottawa, NGC, 1953, No. 26
Stratford, Ont., 1964
Saint John, NBM,
Jack Humphrey, 1965, No. 9
Reproduced
CA, vol. v, 1947, p. 65

JACKSON, ALEXANDER YOUNG (1882–)

56
Georgian Bay, November (ca. 1921)
oil on canvas
26 x 32
signed lower right: A. Y. JACKSON
Purchased by the House Committee, 1922
Literature
A. H. Robson, *A. Y. Jackson* (1938), p. 11
Harper (1955), p. 11 (repr. in colour)
A. Y. Jackson, *A Painter's Country* (1958), p. 72
Exhibitions
Toronto, OSA, 1922, No. 27
Montreal, Dominion Gallery, 1946
Toronto AGT, 1949, No. 52
Boston, 1949, No. 42 (illus. p. 32)
Toronto, AGT, *A. Y. Jackson*, 1953, No. 36 (illus. p. 8)
Reproduced
Buchanan (1950), pl. 14
CA, vol. v, 1947, p. 64

57
Labrador Coast (1928)
oil on canvas
50 x 61
signed lower right: A. Y. JACKSON
Purchased with the income from the Harold and Murray Wrong Memorial Fund, 1941
Literature
Harper (1955), p. 32
Exhibitions
Toronto, AGT, 1928, No. 30
RCA, 1930, No. 94 (illus.)
St. Louis, 1930, No. 32
Ottawa, NGC, 1931, No. 137
Vancouver, VAG, 1966, No. 76
Reproduced
CA, vol. xix, 1962, p. 431

58
October Morning, Algoma
(formerly known as
Wartz Lake, Algoma)
oil on canvas
52 x 60
signed and dated lower left:
A. Y. JACKSON *'20*
Purchased by the House Committee, 1931–2
Literature
A. H. Robson, *A. Y. Jackson* (1938), p. 11
Harper (1955), p. 26
A. Y. Jackson, *A Painter's Country* (1958), p. 46
Lawren Harris, *The Group of Seven* (1964), p. 20
Exhibitions
London, British Empire Exhibition, 1924 (Canadian Section)
Paris, Jeu de Paume, 1927, No. 87
RCA, 1927, No. 97
St. Louis, 1930, No. 31
Ottawa, NGC, 1936, No. 107
San Francisco, 1939, No. 12 (Canadian Section)
Vancouver, VAG, 1954, No. 34 (illus.)

JARVIS, LUCY (1896–)

59
Children and Ducks (1948)
oil on composition board
16 x 20
signed lower left: LUCY JARVIS
Purchased by the Art Committee, 1949–50

KIYOOKA, ROY (1926–)

60
The Ring and the Window
aquatex on canvas
52 x 55
signed lower right:
R. KIYOOKA *'66*
Selected by the Art Committee, 1966–7, in memory of Larry Greenspan, Secretary of the Art Committee 1964–6, and presented to Hart House by his friends

KRIEGHOFF, CORNELIUS (1815–72)

61
Coureur de bois (ca. 1860)
oil on canvas
11 x 9
signed lower right:
C. KRIEGHOFF
Presented by Mrs. V. E. Henderson in Memory of Dr. V. E. Henderson, 1950
Literature
Harper (1955), p. 5

62
Moccasin Seller (ca. 1860)
oil on canvas
11 x 9
signed lower right centre:
C. KRIEGHOFF
Presented by Mrs. V. E. Henderson in Memory of Dr. V. E. Henderson, 1950

LACROIX, RICHARD (1939–)

63
Variante (1965)
acrylic and oil on canvas
32 x 32
Purchased by the Art Committee, 1965–6

LEMIEUX, JEAN-PAUL (1904–)

64
La chandaille rouge
oil on canvas
47 x 20½
signed and dated upper right:
JEAN PAUL LEMIEUX *58*
Purchased by the Art Committee, 1959–60
Exhibitions
Stratford, Ont., 1959, No. 5
Montreal, MMFA, *Jean-Paul Lemieux*, 1967, No. 44

LEVINE, LES (1936–)

65
Drawing IV (1964)
acrylic on paper
23½ x 18½
Purchased by the Art Committee, 1964–5

62

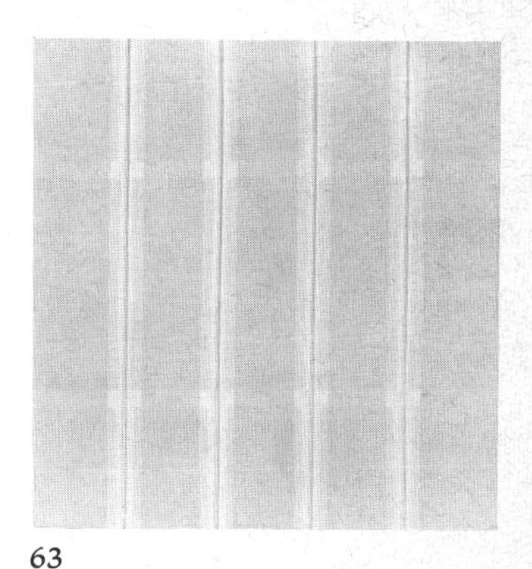

63

67

68

69

70

LISMER, ARTHUR (1885–1969)

66
Isles of Spruce
oil on canvas
47 x 64
signed and dated lower left:
A. LISMER 22
Purchased by the Sketch Committee, 1927–8
Literature
Housser (1926), p. 152, 178; repr. p. 188
Harper (1955), p. 31 (repr. in colour)
J. A. B. McLeish, *A September Gale* (1955), pp. 72, 76, 203
Lawren Harris, *The Group of Seven* (1964), p. 20
Exhibitions
Toronto, CNE, 1922, No. 267 (illus. p. 39)
RCA, 1922, No. 128
RCA, 1924, No. 124
London, British Empire Exhibition, 1924 (Canadian Section)
London, Whitechapel AG, 1925, No. 23
Manchester, AG, 1926, No. 126
Paris, Jeu de Paume, 1927, No. 108
Toronto, AGT, 1928, No. 46
St. Louis, 1930, No. 34
San Francisco, 1939, No. 14 (Canadian Section)
Toronto, AGT, *Arthur Lismer*, 1950, No. 10 (illus. pl. 6)
Hamilton, AGH, 1953, No. 31 (illus.)
Vancouver, VAG, 1954, No. 45 (illus.)
Vancouver, VAG, 1966, No. 80 (illus.)
Reproduced
CA, vol. XX, 1963, p. 218

67
Boat Builder (1927)
pencil
13 x 10 (sight)
signed lower left: A.L.
Gift of H. L. Rous

68
Mme F. X. Cimon
pencil
10 x 13 (sight)
signed and dated lower right:
A. LISMER 27
Gift of the Artist, 1928

69
Napoléon Le Blond
pencil
9 x 12 (sight)
signed and dated lower right:
A. LISMER MAY/27
Gift of the Artist, 1928

70
M. et Mme La Plante
pencil
9 x 13 (sight)
signed and dated lower right:
A. LISMER/27 MAY
Gift of the Artist, 1928

LOVEROFF, F. M. (1894–)

71
Break in the Woods (1921)
oil on canvas
22 x 20
signed lower left:
F. M. LOVEROFF
Purchased by the House Committee, 1922–3

72
Sunset (ca. 1922)
oil on canvas
20 x 22
signed lower left: F. M. LOVEROFF
Purchased by the House Committee, 1922–3

MACDONALD, GRANT KENNETH (1909–)

73
Girl in White
oil on gesso ground panel
25 x 20
signed and dated lower right:
GRANT MACDONALD '53
Purchased by the Art Committee, 1952–3

MACDONALD, J. E. H. (1873–1932)

74
Larch Trees (ca. 1929)
oil on cardboard
8½ x 10½

75
Laurentian Village
oil on canvas
28½ x 36
signed and dated lower right:
J. E. H. MACDONALD '16
Gift of the Graduating Year of 1925
Literature
Housser (1926), p. 110
A. H. Robson, *J. E. H. MacDonald* (1937), p. 11
E. R. Hunter, *J. E. H. MacDonald* (1940), p. 16, 50
Harper (1955), p. 23
Exhibitions
Toronto, CNE, 1916, No. 383
Toronto, OSA, 1916, No. 89
RCA, 1916; No. 148
Saint John, 1920, No. 54
Toronto, AGT, 1922, No. 84
Toronto, AGT, *J. E. H. MacDonald*, 1965, No. 65 (illus.)

76
October Shower Gleam (1922)
oil on canvas
40 x 48
signed and dated lower left:
J. E. H. MACDONALD '22
Purchased with the income from the Harold and Murray Wrong Memorial Fund, 1933
Literature
E. R. Hunter, *J. E. H. MacDonald* (1940), pp. 26, 53
Thoreau MacDonald, *The Group of Seven* (1944), see footnote p. 5
Buchanan (1950), pl. 21
Harper (1955), p. 29 (repr. in colour)
J. A. B. McLeish, *A September Gale* (1955), p. 76
A. Y. Jackson, *A Painter's Country* (1958), p. 46
Exhibitions
Toronto, CNE, 1922, No. 274
RCA, 1922, No. 136
Toronto, AGT, 1922, No. 12
Worcester, Mass., 1924, No. 20
London, British Empire Exhibition, 1925 (Canadian Section)
London, Whitechapel AG, 1925, No. 5
Manchester, AG, 1926, No. 104
Paris, Jeu de Paume, 1927, No. 125
Buffalo, 1928, No. 40
Calgary, 1929, No. 103
St. Louis, 1930, No. 38
Ottawa, NGC, 1936, No. 158
San Francisco, 1939, No. 17 (Canadian Section)
Boston, 1949, No. 54
Washington, 1950, No. 52 (illus.)
Hamilton, AGH, 1953, No. 33
Vancouver, VAG, 1954, No. 55
Toronto, AGT, *J. E. H. MacDonald*, 1965, No. 38 (illus.)

71

72

74

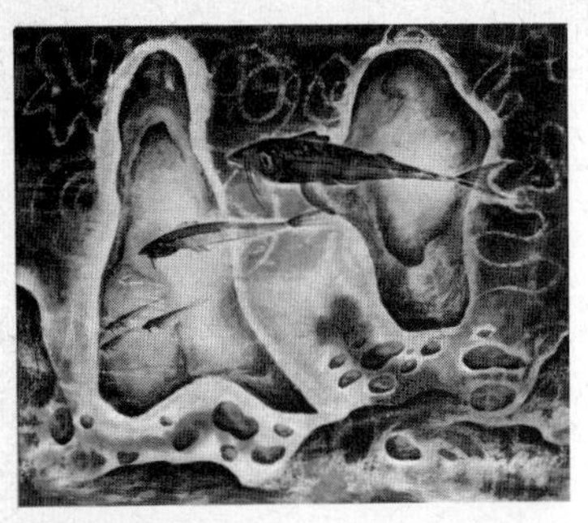

78

79

82

MACDONALD, J. W. G. (JOCK)
(1897–1960)

77
Airy Journey
oil on canvas
42 x 48
signed and dated lower left:
JOCK MACDONALD *57*
Purchased by the Art Committee, 1961–2

78
Fish Family
water colour
15 x 18
signed and dated lower right:
J. W. G. MACDONALD DEC. *1943*
Purchased by the Art Committee, 1949–50
Literature
Harper (1955), p. 68
Exhibitions
Toronto, AGT, 1950, No. 207

MACDONALD, THOREAU (1901–)

79
Oiling the Plough, November
pen and ink, wash
13 x 18
signed and dated lower right:
T.M. *'49*
Purchased by the Art Committee, 1949–50
Literature
Harper (1955), p. 71

MCEWEN, JEAN (1923–)

80
La Victoire de Sardanapale
(reworked 1966)
oil on canvas
30 x 30
Purchased by the Art Committee, 1966–7

MASSON, HENRI (1907–)

81
The Artist
oil on canvas
26 x 30
signed and dated lower right
centre: HENRI MASSON/*41*
Gift of the Graduating Year
of 1941
Literature
Harper (1955), p. 60
Exhibitions
Toronto, AGT, *CGP*, 1942, No. 33
Toronto, CNE, 1950, No. 119

82
Ice Harvest
oil on canvas
18 x 21
signed and dated lower left
centre: HENRI MASSON *37*
Gift of the Graduating Year
of 1939
Exhibitions
Toronto, OSA, 1937, No. 116
RCA, 1937, No. 146
Toronto, CNE, 1949, No. 74

MILNE, DAVID BROWN
(1882–1953)

83
Water Lillies, Temagami (1928)
oil on canvas
20 x 24
Gift of the Rt. Hon. Vincent
Massey, CH, 1947
Literature
Buchanan (1950), p. 66, pl. 42
Harper (1955), p. 50
Dept. of Immigration, *The Arts in Canada* (1957), p. 89
A. H. Jarvis, *David Milne* (1962), p. 9, pl. 15
Hubbard (1963), p. 105, pl. 181
Harper (1966), p. 232, pl. 292
Exhibitions
Boston, 1949, No. 64
Washington, 1950, No. 58
(illus.)
Ottawa, NGC, 1953, No. 49
Ottawa, NGC, *David Milne*,
1953, No. 28
Toronto, Laing Galleries,
1959, No. 26 (illus.)
Ottawa, NGC, 1967, No. 230

84
Beyond the Point (1948)
water colour
14 x 20
Purchased by the Art Committee, 1947–8

85
Scaffolding (1946)
water colour
14 x 21 (sight)
Gift of the Graduating Year of 1948
Literature
Harper (1955), p. 61

86
Adirondack Valley (1941)
drypoint
5 x 6⅞
signed lower left:
DAVID MILNE
Gift of the Medical Society, 1956

87
Main Street (1942)
drypoint
6⅞ x 8⅞
signed lower left:
DAVID MILNE
Gift of the Victoria College Union, 1956

88
Outlet of the Pond (1925–30)
drypoint
6⅞ x 8⅞
signed lower left:
DAVID MILNE
Gift of the Engineering Society, 1956

89
St. Michael's Cathedral (1943)
drypoint
7⅜ x 8⅞
signed lower left:
DAVID MILNE
Gift of the Medical Society, 1956

90
Still Water and Fish (1941)
drypoint
6⅞ x 8⅞
signed lower left:
DAVID MILNE
Gift of the Graduating Year, School of Architecture, 1956

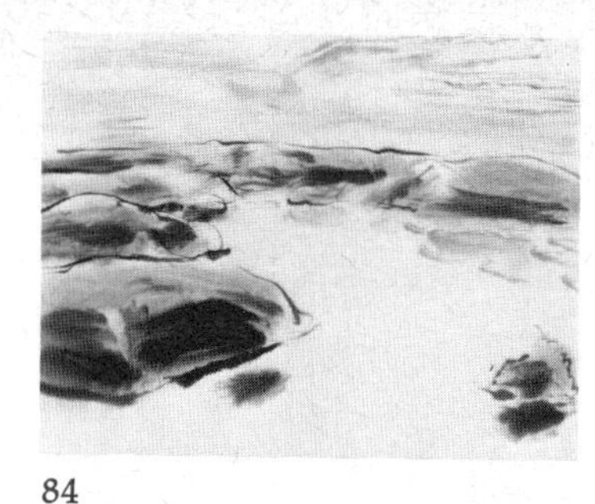
84

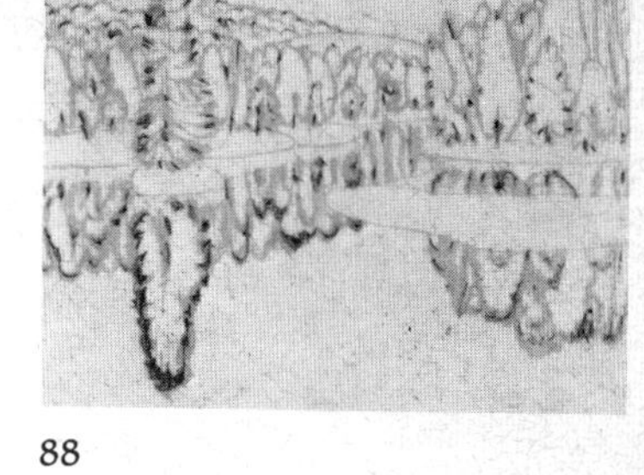
88

86

89

87

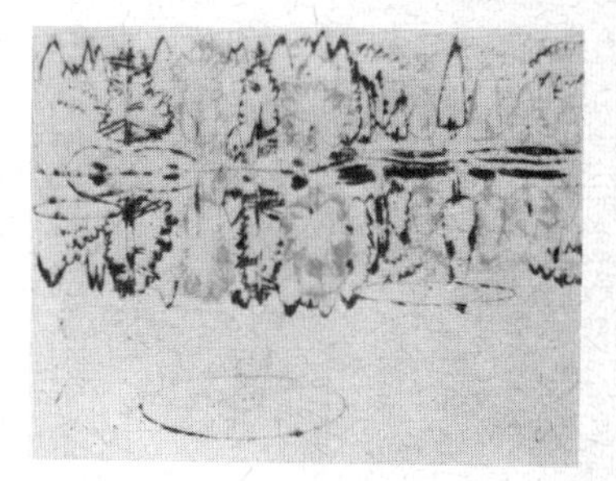
90

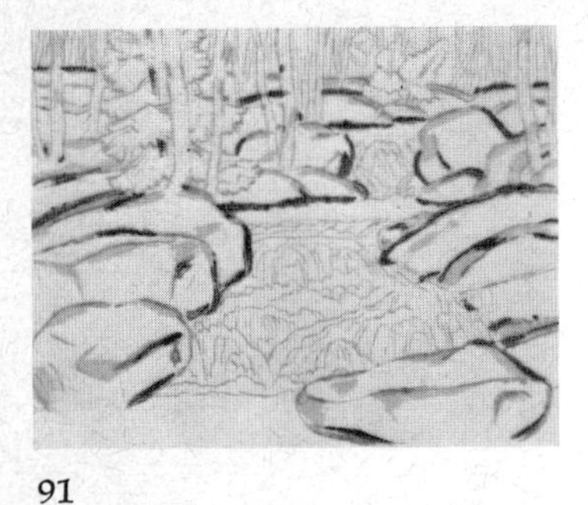
91

92

95

97

MILNE, DAVID BROWN
(1882–1953)

91
Waterfall
drypoint
6⅞ x 8⅞
signed lower left:
DAVID MILNE
Gift of the Victoria College
Union, 1956

92
Yard of the Queen's Hotel (1937)
drypoint
6⅞ x 8⅞
signed lower left:
DAVID MILNE
Gift of the Engineering
Society, 1956

MOLINARI, GUIDO (1933–)

93
Espace jaune
acrylic and latex on canvas
60 x 72
signed and dated lower right:
MOLINARI *61*
Purchased by the Art Committee, 1965–6

MORRICE, JAMES WILSON
(1865–1924)

94
Algiers (1922)
9 x 11½
Purchased from the Print Fund,
1927
Literature
Harper (1955), p. 8
Exhibitions
Montreal, MMFA, *J. W. Morrice*,
1965, No. 105
Reproduced
Buchanan (1950), pl. 11
CA, vol. XX, 1963, p. 219

MORRIS, KATHLEEN MOIR
(1894–)

95
Nuns, Quebec (ca. 1926)
oil on canvas
24 x 18
signed lower right: K. M. MORRIS
Purchased by the House Committee, 1934–5
Literature
Harper (1955), p. 46
Exhibitions
RCA, 1926, No. 103
Ottawa, NGC, 1927, No. 162
Toronto, OSA, 1935, No. 136
London, Tate, 1938, No. 163

MORRISEAU, NORVAL (1932–)

96
Fish Cycle (ca. 1963)
tempera
20 x 30
Purchased by the Art Committee, 1964–5

MUHLSTOCK, LOUIS (1904–)

97
Gwen Phillips (1946)
charcoal and chalk
15½ x 13
signed lower right: MUHLSTOCK
Purchased by the Art Committee, 1945–6

NAKAMURA, KAZUO (1926–)

98
Summer Reflections (1957)
oil on masonite
28 x 36
Purchased with income from the Harold and Murray Wrong Memorial Fund, 1958

NEWTON, LILIAS TORRANCE (1896–)

99
Alice Massey (1934)
oil on canvas
46 x 36
signed lower left:
L. TORRANCE NEWTON
Gift of The Hon. Vincent and Mrs. Massey, 1934
Literature
Harper (1955), p. 14

100
Vincent Massey (1934)
oil on canvas
46 x 36
signed lower right:
L. TORRANCE NEWTON
Gift of The Hon. Vincent and Mrs. Massey, 1934
Literature
Harper (1955), p. 15
Exhibitions
?RCA, 1935, No. 196
Toronto, CNE, 1952, No. 15

101
Maurice (1939)
oil on canvas
30 x 24
signed lower right:
L. TORRANCE NEWTON
Purchased with income from the Harold and Murray Wrong Memorial Fund, 1939

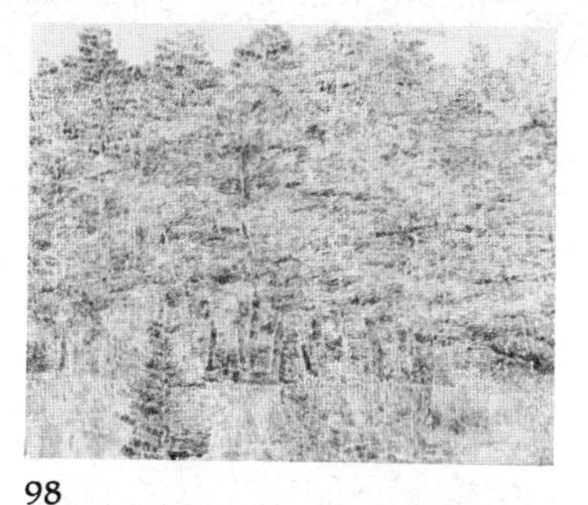
98

99

100

102

103

105

106

NICHOLS, JACK LEONARD
(1921–)

102
Head of a Dancer
coloured chalks
21½ x 16½ (sight)
signed lower left: J. NICHOLS
Purchased with a gift, courtesy of Lois Marshall and Weldon Kilburn

103
Medieval Presence
Lithograph
21 x 17 (sight)
signed and dated lower right:
J. NICHOLS *58*
Purchased by the Art Committee, 1961

104
Pierrot with Ball
lithograph
19½ x 16½ (sight)
signed and dated lower right:
J. NICHOLS *1957*
Purchased by the Art Committee, 1961

NORWELL, GRAHAM NOBLE
(1901–67)

105
Birches, Rockcliffe
oil on canvas
38 x 42
signed and dated lower right:
NORWELL 22
Gift of the Graduating Year of 1923
Exhibitions
Toronto, OSA, 1923, No. 135

106
Camping Scene (also known as *Autumn Camp*)
oil on canvas
61 x 64
signed and dated lower right:
NORWELL *23*
Gift of the Graduating Year of 1928
Exhibitions
Toronto, CNE, No. 217
(illus. p. 36)

OGILVIE, WILL A. (1901–)

107
Hart House Chapel Murals
Commissioned by the Massey Foundation and placed on the walls of the Chapel in 1936
Reproduced
B. Brooker, *Yearbook of the Arts* (1936), pl. 88
The Studio, vol. cxiv, No. 533, 1937, p. 72

108
Glacier and Lake (1957)
water colour, pen and ink
15 x 22
signed lower right:
WILL OGILVIE
Gift of the Society of Geodesists and Geophysicists, 1957

PALMER, HERBERT S. (1881–)

109
Golden October (1918)
oil on canvas
24 x 36
signed lower left:
H. S. PALMER
Gift of the Graduating Year of 1922
Exhibitions
Toronto, OSA, 1922, No. 142

PANTON, L. A. C. (1894–1954)

110
Haliburton Impressions (1938)
oil on canvas
19 x 23
signed lower right: PANTON
Purchased by the Arts Committee, 1949–50
Literature
Harper (1955), p. 57

111
Untitled (ca. 1953)
oil on masonite
30 x 36
Purchased by the Art Committee, 1955–6

PARKER, HARLEY W. B. (1915–)

112
Dugout (1942)
water colour
8½ x 11
signed lower right:
H. PARKER
Purchased by Hart House, 1942
Exhibitions
Hart House, *Canadian Armed Forces Art Exhibition*, 1942

PELLAN, ALFRED (1906–)

113
La fenêtre ouverte (1936)
oil on canvas
17½ x 32
signed lower right: PELLAN
Gift of Charles E. McFaddin, 1964
Exhibitions
Saint John, NBM, 1967, No. 35 (illus.)

PEPPER, GEORGE D. (1903–62)

114
Tobacco Patch (1938–9)
oil on canvas
25 x 29
signed lower right: PEPPER
Gift of the Graduating Year of 1940
Literature
Harper (1955), p. 58

108

109

110

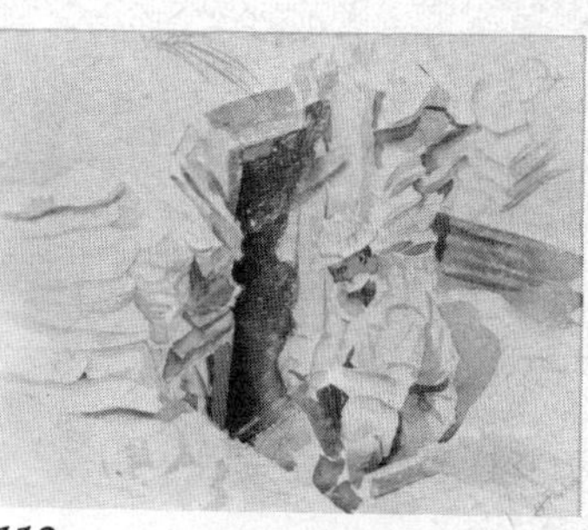
112

114

115

117

116

118

120

PFLUG, CHRISTIANE (1936–)

115
Railway Yards in the Rain (1962)
oil on canvas
19½ x 22
signed lower right: C. PFLUG
Purchased by the Art Committee, 1962–3
Exhibitions
Winnipeg, WAG, *Christiane Pflug*, 1966, No. 9

PHILLIPS, WALTER J. (1884–1963)

116
Howe Sound
water colour
14 x 18
signed and dated lower right:
W. J. PHILLIPS *35*
Gift of the Graduating Year of 1936

117
Mamalilicoola, B.C. (1928)
colour woodblock
12 x 14
signed lower right:
W. J. PHILLIPS
Purchased from the Print Fund, 1928
Literature
Harper (1955), p. 11

118
Mountain Torrent (1926)
colour woodblock
8½ x 12
signed lower right:
W. J. PHILLIPS
Purchased from the Print Fund, 1928

119
York Boat on Lake Winnipeg
colour woodblock
10 x 14
signed lower right:
W. J. PHILLIPS
Purchased from the Print Fund, 1955

PLAYFAIR, CHARLES (1917–)

120
Prometheus I
conté crayon
21 x 16
signed and dated lower left:
PLAYFAIR *49*
Purchased by the Art Committee, 1950–51
Literature
Harper (1955), p. 76

RAKINE, MARTHE

121
MacKellar I
oil on canvas
29½ x 23
signed and dated lower right:
M. RAKINE *1950*
Purchased by the Art Committee, 1950–1
Literature
Harper (1955), p. 81
(repr. in colour)

REPPEN, JACK (1933–64)

122
Four p.m. in the Plaza, Mexico
oil and gesso on masonite
48 x 36
signed and dated lower right:
REPPEN *63*
Purchased by the Art Committee, 1962–3

ROBERTS, WILLIAM GOODRIDGE
(1904–)

123
House on a Hilltop (1950)
oil on canvas
23½ x 35
signed lower right: G. ROBERTS
Purchased by the Art Committee, 1950–1
Literature
Harper (1955), p. 77
(repr. in colour)

124
Portrait of a Girl (1938)
oil on canvas
27 x 18
signed lower right: G. ROBERTS
Gift of the Graduating Years of 1946 and 1947
Literature
Harper (1955), p. 67
Exhibitions
Toronto, CNE, 1949, No. 15
Reproduced
CA, vol. V, 1947, p. 64

ROBERTS, WILLIAM GRIFFITH
(1921–)

125
The Long Pier No. 2 (1960)
oil on masonite
23 x 9
signed lower left:
WILLIAM ROBERTS
Purchased by the Art Committee, 1960–1
Exhibitions
Toronto, OSA, 1960, No. 62
Reproduced
CA, vol. XX, 1963, p. 219

SANDERS, BENITA (1935–)

126
Ziggurat
intaglio print
19 x 19½ (sight)
signed and dated lower right:
BENITA SANDERS *1966*
Purchased by the Art Committee, 1966–7

121

123

125

127

129

128

131

SAVAGE, ANNE D. (1897–)

127
Spruce Swamp (1929)
oil on canvas
20 x 24
signed lower left:
A. D. SAVAGE
Gift of the Graduating Year of 1930
Literature
Harper (1955), p. 57

SCHAEFER, CARL (1903–)

128
Field Edge and Plain
water colour
22½ x 28
signed and dated lower right:
C. SCHAEFER *26.7.58*
Purchased with income from the Harold and Murray Wrong Memorial Fund, 1959
Reproduced
CA, vol. xvii, 1960, p. 71

129
R.R. No. 3, Hanover
water colour
26½ x 28
signed and dated lower centre:
CARL SCHAEFER *1936*
Purchased by the House Committee, 1935–6
Literature
Harper (1955), p. 54

SHADBOLT, JACK LEONARD (1909–)

130
Northern Elegy No. 2
oil and lucite on canvas
39 x 49
signed and dated lower right:
SHADBOLT *'64*
Purchased by the Art Committee, 1964–5
Reproduced
CA, vol. xxii, 1965, p. 63

SHONIKER, CLAIRE

131
Five Foolish Virgins
etching
8 x 10
signed and dated lower right:
CLAIRE SHONIKER/*57*
Purchased by the Art Committee, 1956–7

SKELTON, JOHN (1887–)

132
*Ramilles** (1942)
oil on canvas
16 x 20
Purchased by Hart House, 1942
Exhibitions
Hart House, *Canadian Armed Forces Art Exhibition*, 1942

SMITH, GORDON APPLEBY (1919–)

133
Rocks with Yellow (1957)
oil on cotton
23 x 40
signed lower right: SMITH
Purchased by the Art Committee, 1958

SMITH, W. ST. THOMAS (1862–1947)

134
Fishermen's Homes, Fife Coast, Scotland (1923)
water colour
16 x 23
signed lower left:
W. ST. THOMAS SMITH
Gift of the Class of '98 Arts in 1923

STAPLETON, W. J. (1916–)

135
*Canadian Airman** (1942)
oil on canvas
30 x 20
Purchased by Hart House, 1942
Exhibitions
Hart House, *Canadian Armed Forces Art Exhibition*, 1942

STEVENS, DOROTHY (1890–)

136
*Bridges**
etching
9¾ x 9¾

137
*Figures in Chartres**
etching
8 x 3⅛

138
*Railroad Shops**
etching
24½ x 21
Purchased by the Sketch Committee, 1934

TEITLEBAUM, MASHEL (1921–)

139
Heraldic Gold (1966)
acrylic and oil on canvas
50 x 40
Purchased by the Art Committee, 1966–7

THOMSON, TOM (1877–1917)

140
Birches (ca. 1912)
oil on composition board
9 x 11
signed lower right:
TOM THOMSON
(authenticated and signed by J. E. H. MacDonald)
Purchased with the income from the Harold and Murray Wrong Memorial Fund, 1929
Literature
Harper (1955), p. 22

134

142

143

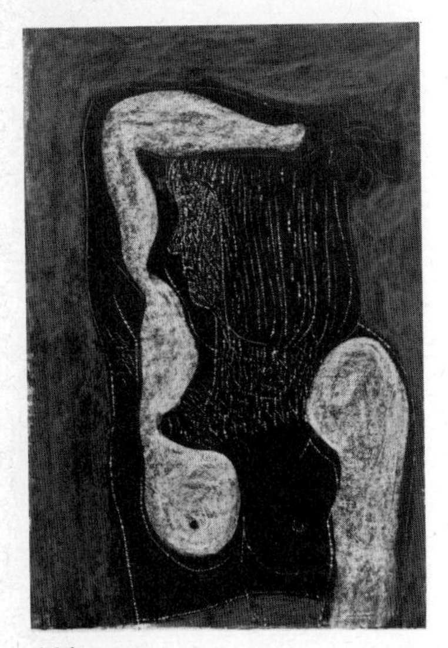
146

THOMSON, TOM (1877–1917)

141
The Pointers (also known as *Pageant of the North*) (1915)
oil on canvas
40 x 45½
Purchased by the House Committee and with the Print Fund, 1928–9
Literature
Blodwen Davies, *Tom Thomson* (1935), p. 112
A. H. Robson, *Tom Thomson* (1937), p. 9
Audrey Saunders, *The Algonquin Story* (1948), p. 172
Harper (1955), p. 21 (repr. in colour)
R. H. Hubbard, *Tom Thomson* (1962), p. 21
(detail repr. in colour on cover)
Hubbard (1963), pp. 89, 91
Harper (1966), p. 282, pl. 251 (colour)
Exhibitions
Toronto, AGT, 1920, No. 25
London, British Empire Exhibition, 1925 (Canadian Section)
London, Whitechapel AG, 1925, No. 28
Manchester, AG, 1926, No. 167
Ottawa, NGC, 1932, No. 8
London, Tate, 1938, No. 207 (illus.)
Boston, 1949, No. 91
Washington, 1950, No. 79
Toronto, CNE, 1950, No. 22
Ottawa, NGC, 1953, No. 65
Vancouver, VAG, 1954, No. 64
Windsor, Willistead AG, 1957, No. 12
Mexico City, 1960, No. 115
London, Ont., LPL, 1965, No. 30
Ottawa, NGC, 1967, No. 195 (illus.)
Reproduced
CA, vol v, 1947, p. 63
Buchanan (1945), pl. 38
R. H. Hubbard, *Anthology of Canadian Art* (1960), pl. 93 (colour)

142
Rock, Birches and Sunlight (1916–7)
oil on panel
8½ x 10½
signed lower right centre:
TOM THOMSON
Purchased with the income from the Harold and Murray Wrong Memorial Fund, 1929
Literature
Harper (1955), p. 22

TONNANCOUR, JACQUES G. DE (1917–)

143
At the Foot of the Mountain
oil on masonite
15 x 22
signed and dated lower right:
DE TONNANCOUR/*63*
Purchased by the Art Committee, 1963–4
Reproduced
CA, vol. XXI, 1964, p. 306

144
The Blue Dress
oil on canvas
35 x 25
signed and dated upper right:
DE TONNANCOUR *13.3.44*
Purchased by the House Committee, 1943–4
Literature
Harper (1955), p. 69
Exhibitions
Toronto, AGT, 1945, No. 214 (illus.)
Reproduced
Dept. of Immigration, *The Arts in Canada* (1965), p. 110

TOWN, HAROLD (1924–)

145
Homage to Turner
oil on canvas
68 x 79
signed and dated lower right:
TOWN *60*
Purchased by the Art Committee, 1961–2
Reproduced
CA, vol. XX, 1963, p. 215

146
Study for Atreus (1963)
charcoal and pastel on paper
22 x 15
Purchased by the House Committee, 1963–4

URQUHART, TONY (1934–)

147
Green Field
oil wash and inks
11 x 17
signed and dated lower right:
URQUHART *1962*
Purchased by the Art Committee, 1962–3

148
Rock and Leaves
oil wash and inks
11 x 17
signed and dated lower right:
URQUHART/*62*
Purchased by the Art Committee, 1962–3

VARLEY, FREDERICK H. (1881–)

149
Huntley Gordon
oil on composition board
10 x 13½
Gift of the Estate of Huntley Gordon, 1961

150
Magic Tree (1925)
oil on panel
21 x 21
signed lower right: VARLEY
Purchased by the House Committee, 1924–5

151
*Chester Massey**
oil on canvas
47½ x 56
signed and dated lower left:
F. H. VARLEY *1920*
Owned by the University of Toronto, on loan to Hart House
Literature
Harper (1955), p. 28
Exhibitions
RCA, 1920, No. 248
Toronto, OSA, 1921, No. 143 (illus.)
Vancouver, VAG, 1966, No. 74
Saint John, NBM, 1967, No. 29

152
Vincent Massey
oil on canvas
47 x 56
signed and dated lower left:
F. H. VARLEY *1920*
Presented to Vincent Massey by his friends in the University of Toronto on the occasion of the completion of Hart House

Literature
N. M. MacTavish, *The Fine Arts in Canada* (1925), p. 134
Hubbard (1963), p. 95
Harper (1966), p. 295
Exhibitions
Toronto, CNE, 1920, no. 135 (illus., p. 30; repr. on cover)
London, British Empire Exhibition, 1924, No. 251 (Canadian Section)
Ottawa, NGC, 1936, No. 182
Ottawa, NGC, 1967, No. 209 (illus.)
Reproduced
CA, vol. xii, 1954, p. 5
Hubbard (1960), pl. 83

147

148

149

154

156

VARLEY, FREDERICK H. (1881–)

153
Self Portrait (ca. 1945)
oil on canvas
19 x 15½
signed lower left: VARLEY
Purchased by the Art Committee, 1949–50
Literature
Harper (1955), p. 37
(repr. in colour)
Exhibitions
Toronto, OSA, 1946, No. 145
Toronto, CNE, 1949, No. 19
Reproduced
CA, vol. XX, 1963, p. 220

154
Dr. Hardolph Wastenys (1950)
oil on canvas
40 x 34
signed lower left: VARLEY
Purchased by Hart House, 1950
Literature
Harper (1955), p. 38
Exhibitions
Toronto, AGT, *CGP*, 1950, No. 89

155
Open Window (ca. 1933)
oil on canvas 40 x 43
signed lower right: VARLEY
Purchased with income from the Harold and Murray Wrong Memorial Fund, 1944
Literature
Harper (1955), p. 36
Harper (1966), p. 295
Exhibitions
Toronto, CNE, 1933, No. 176

156
Eskimo Boy (1938)
pencil
9 x 10
Reproduced
Edmund Carpenter, *Eskimo*, 1959
CA, vol. XVI, 1959, p. 97

WATSON, HOMER (1855–1935)

157
Pines in Winter (ca. 1935)
oil on composition board
12 x 16
signed lower left: HOMER WATSON
Purchased by the House Committee, 1936–7
Literature
Harper (1955), p. 7

WATSON, SYDNEY H. (1911–)

158
City, Back Elevation (ca. 1950)
oil on linen
25 x 35
signed lower right: SYDNEY H. WATSON
Purchased with income from the Harold and Murray Wrong Memorial Fund, 1952
Literature
Harper (1955), p. 22
Exhibitions
Toronto, CNE, 1950, No. 97
RCA, 1951, No. 92 (illus.)

WEBBER, GORDON (1909–)

159
*Design No. 5, Vermont, 1947**
tempera and ink
19 x 28
Purchased by the Art Committee, 1947–8
Literature
Harper (1955), p. 75

WESTON, WILLIAM P. (1879–)

160
Cheam
42 x 48
signed and dated lower left:
W. P. WESTON *'33*
Purchased by the House Committee, 1933–4
Literature
Wm. Colgate, *Canadian Art* (1943), p. 192
Harper (1955), p. 52
Exhibitions
Toronto, AGT, 1945, No. 168
Vancouver, VAG, *Weston*, 1959

WILSON, R. YORK (1907–)

161
Honfleur (1962)
oil on canvas
38 x 54
signed lower right:
YORK WILSON
Purchased through a private donation, May 1964

WOOD, WILLIAM J. (1877–1954)

162
Memory's Melodies
oil on canvas
36 x 26
signed and dated upper left:
W. J. WOOD *1919*
Purchased by the Art Committee, 1935
Literature
Harper (1955), p. 45
Exhibitions
Atlantic City, 1933, No. 61
New York, 1939, No. 64 (Canadian Section)

YOUNG, NORMAN (1901–1942)

163
*Sunrise over Bishopstone** (ca. 1942)
pastel
14 x 18
Purchased with income from the Harold and Murray Wrong Memorial Fund, 1945

157

161

160

162

Abbreviations: *Literature*

CA Canadian Art (periodical)
Buchanan (1950) D. W. Buchanan *The Growth of Canadian Painting*
Harper (1955) J. Russell Harper *Canadian Paintings in Hart House*
Harper (1966) J. Russell Harper *Painting in Canada*
Housser (1926) F. B. Housser *A Canadian Art Movement*
Hubbard (1963) R. H. Hubbard *The Development of Canadian Art*

Abbreviations: *Art Galleries and Museums*

AGH Art Gallery of Hamilton
AGT Art Gallery of Toronto (now Art Gallery of Ontario)
LPL London Public Library and Art Museum
MMFA Montreal Museum of Fine Arts
NBM New Brunswick Museum
NGC National Gallery of Canada
VAG Vancouver Art Gallery
WAG Winnipeg Art Gallery

Abbreviations: *Exhibitions*

(illus.) reproduced in catalogue of exhibition

Andover, Mass., 1942 *Contemporary Painting in Canada* (Phillips Academy)
Atlantic City, 1933 *Paintings of the Canadian Group of Painters* (Heinz Art Salon)
Boston, 1949 *Forty Years of Canadian Painting* (Museum of Fine Arts)
Buffalo, 1928 *Exhibition of Paintings by Canadian Artists* (Fine Arts Academy)
Calgary, 1929 *Calgary Exhibition and Stampede* (The Art Gallery)
Hamilton, AGH, 1953 *Inaugural Exhibition*
London, British Empire Exhibition, 1924 and 1925 *Canadian Fine Arts Section* (Wembley)
London, Whitechapel AG, 1926 *Exhibition of Canadian Art*
London, Tate, 1938 *A Century of Canadian Art* (Tate Gallery)
London, Ont., LPL, 1965 *Canadian Impressionists*
Manchester, 1926 *Exhibition of Canadian Picture* (Manchester Art Gallery)
Mexico City, 1960 *Arte Canadiense*
New Haven, Yale University, 1944 *Canadian Art 1760–1943*
New York, 1939 *World's Fair* (Fine Arts Gallery)
New York, Canadian Club, 1948
Exhibition of Contemporary Canadian Art (Waldorf Astoria)
Ottawa, NGC
1927 *Annual Exhibition of Canadian Art*
1931 *Annual Exhibition of Canadian Art*
1932 *Annual Exhibition of Canadian Art*
1936 *Retrospective Exhibition of Paintings by the Group of Seven*
1953 *Exhibition of Canadian Paintings to celebrate the Coronation of Her Majesty Queen Elizabeth II*
1967 *Three Hundred Years of Canadian Art*
Paris, Jeu de Paume, 1927 *Exposition d'art canadien* (Musée de Jeu de Paume)
Port Arthur, Lakehead College, 1964 *The Group of Seven and Lake Superior*
Philadelphia, 1926 *Sesqui-Centennial International Exposition*
Richmond, Va., 1949 *Exhibition of Canadian Painting 1668–1948* (Virginia Museum)
Rio de Janeiro, 1944 *Pintura canadense contemporanea* (Museo nacional de belas artes)
San Francisco, 1939 *Golden Gate International Exposition*
Saint John, 1920 *Paintings by Canadian Artists* (Saint John Art Club)
Saint John, NBM, 1967 *Ten Decades; Ten Painters*
St. Louis, 1930 *An Exhibition of Paintings by Contemporary Canadian Artists* (City Art Museum)
Stratford, Ont., 1964 *Faces of Canada* (Stratford Festival Exhibition)
Toronto, AGT
1920 *Memorial Exhibition of Paintings by Tom Thomson*
1922 *An Exhibition of Paintings by the Group of Seven*
1926 *An Exhibition of Canadian Paintings*
1928 *An Exhibition of Paintings by the Group of Seven*
1945 *The Development of Painting in Canada*
1950 *Contemporary Canadian Arts*
Toronto, Laing Galleries, 1959 *One Hundred Years of Canadian Painting*
Vancouver, VAG
1954 *The Group of Seven*
1966 *Images for a Canadian Heritage*
Winnipeg, WAG, 1921 *Canadian Art Today*
Windsor, Ont., Willistead AG, 1957 *Tom Thomson*
Worcester, Mass., 1924 *Exhibition of Paintings by Canadian Artists* (Worcester Art Museum)

Bibliography

BROOKER, B. *Yearbook of the Arts in Canada*. Toronto: Macmillan Co., 1929. 306 pp., illus.

——— *Yearbook of the Arts in Canada*. Toronto: Macmillan Co., 1936. 256 pp., illus.

BUCHANAN, D. W. *Canadian Painters*. Oxford and London: Phaidon Press, 1945. 25 pp., illus.

——— *The Growth of Canadian Painting*. Toronto: Collins, 1950. 112 pp., illus.

COLGATE, WILLIAM *Canadian Art: Its Origin and Development*. Toronto: Ryerson Press, 1943. 278 pp., illus.

DAVIES, BLODWEN *A Study of Tom Thomson*. Toronto: Discus Press, 1935. 141 pp., illus.

DUVAL, PAUL *Alfred Joseph Casson*. Toronto: Ryerson Press, 1951. 64 pp., illus.

——— *Canadian Water-Colour Painting*. Toronto: Burns and MacEachern Ltd., 1954. Illus.

HARPER, J. RUSSELL *Canadian Paintings in Hart House*. Toronto: Hart House Art Committee, 1955. 90 pp., illus.

——— *Painting in Canada: A History*. Toronto: University of Toronto Press, 1966. 443 pp., illus.

HARRIS, LAWREN *The Story of the Group of Seven*. Toronto: Rous and Mann, 1964. 29 pp., illus.

HOOVER, DOROTHY *J. W. Beatty*. Toronto: Ryerson Press, 1944. 34 pp., illus.

HOUSSER, P. B. *A Canadian Art Movement: The Story of the "Group of Seven."* Toronto: Macmillan Co., 1926. 221 pp., illus.

HUBBARD, R. H. *Tom Thomson*. Toronto: The Society for Art Publications/McClelland and Stewart, 1962. 30 pp., illus.

——— *The Development of Canadian Art*. Ottawa: The National Gallery of Canada, 1963. 137 pp., illus.

HUNTER, E. R. *J. E. H. MacDonald*. Toronto: Ryerson Press, 1960. 74 pp., illus.

JACKSON, A. Y. *Banting as an Artist*. Toronto: Ryerson Press, 1943. 37 pp., illus.

——— *A Painter's Country*. Toronto: Clarke, Irwin & Co., 1958. 170 pp., illus.

JARVIS, ALAN *David Milne*. Toronto: The Society for Art Publications/McClelland and Stewart Ltd., 1962. 30 pp., illus.

MacDONALD, THOREAU *The Group of Seven*. Toronto: Ryerson Press, 1944. 34 pp., illus.

MCLEISH, J. A. B. *A September Gale.* Toronto: J. M. Dent & Sons, 1955. 212 pp., illus.
MCTAVISH, N. M. *The Fine Arts in Canada.* Toronto: Macmillan Co., 1925, 181 pp., illus.
PIERCE, LORNE *E. Grace Coombs.* Toronto: Ryerson Press, 1949. 32 pp., illus.
ROBSON, A. H. *A. Y. Jackson.* Toronto: Ryerson Press, 1938. 32 pp., illus.
——— *J. E. H. MacDonald.* Toronto: Ryerson Press, 1937. 32 pp., illus.
——— *Tom Thomson.* Toronto: Ryerson Press, 1937. 32 pp., illus.
SAUNDERS, AUDREY *The Algonquin Story.* Toronto: Ontario Department of Lands and Forests, 1948. 196 pp., illus.

The Sketch and Art Committees of Hart House 1921-69

EX OFFICIO:

J. B. Bickersteth, Warden, 1921–40, 1944–47
J. R. Gilley, Acting Warden, 1940–44
Nicholas Ignatieff, Warden, 1947–52
Joseph McCulley, Warden, 1952–65
E. A. Wilkinson, Acting Warden, 1965–66, Warden, 1966–

SKETCH COMMITTEE

1921–22
PROF. BARKER FAIRLEY
Chairman
K. F. NOXON
Secretary
F. B. BROWN
J. C. JACK
C. W. JEFFERYS
B. S. MCCOOL
J. G. MAGEE
R. OLDFORD
J. L. VAN CAMP
G. R. WALTON

1922–23
PROF. BARKER FAIRLEY
Chairman
J. G. MAGEE
Secretary
F. B. BROWN
E. M. COLEMAN
W. A. HIGGINS
J. C. JACK
C. W. JEFFERYS
B. S. MCCOOL
R. OLDFORD
R. V. SOWERS
J. B. SYMINGTON
G. R. WALTON

1923–24
PROF. BARKER FAIRLEY
Chairman
J. C. JACK
Secretary
E. R. ANGUS
E. M. COLEMAN
W. C. COOPER
H. H. HAGGANS
J. L. HART
PROF. T. HEDMAN
W. A. HIGGINS
J. S. LAWSON
J. RYRIE
R. V. SOWERS

1924–25
PROF. H. WASTENEYS
Chairman
W. A. HIGGINS
Secretary
A. B. CUTHBERT
PROF. BARKER FAIRLEY
J. L. HART
J. C. JACK
K. C. MCCARTHY
W. R. PRITCHARD
G. B. RICHARDSON
R. L. RUTNAM
J. RYRIE
W. A. T. VAN EVERY
F. WOOD

1925–26
PROF. H. WASTENEYS
Chairman
M. J. C. LAZIER
Secretary
P. G. ANDERSON
PROF. BARKER FAIRLEY
H. M. MCLAUGHLIN
D. F. MacLAREN
M. N. O'LEARY
S. V. RAILTON
W. E. SHUTE
C. M. STEWART
W. A. WATSON
W. H. WEBER
J. F. WOODS

1926–27
PROF. H. WASTENEYS
Chairman
M. J. C. LAZIER
Secretary
P. G. ANDERSON
C. N. CARSCALLEN
M. T. dePENCIER
PROF. W. S. FUNNELL
T. W. KELLY
D. F. MacLAREN
F. B. PLEWES
S. V. RAILTON
H. D. SHEPPARD
W. E. SHUTE
H. G. SOWARD
K. D. M. SPENCE

1927–28
PROF. W. S. FUNNELL
Chairman
M. J. C. LAZIER
Secretary
PROF. E. R. ARTHUR
J. R. BRYDEN
V. J. BOURKE
C. N. CARSCALLEN
A. W. B. HEWITT
H. F. JEFFREY
D. F. MacLAREN
R. M. MITCHELL
S. V. RAILTON
B. S. SHENSTONE
W. E. SHUTE

1928–29
PROF. W. S. FUNNELL
Chairman
S. V. RAILTON
Secretary
PROF. E. R. ARTHUR
H. BORSOOK
J. T. BRYDEN
G. L. CASSIDY
A. W. DAVIDSON
M. G. GOULD
L. D. IRWIN
J. D. KEITH
R. M. MITCHELL
W. R. RAMSAY
F. D. SHANNON
L. SHERWOOD

1929–30

PROF. W. S. FUNNELL
Chairman
L. SHERWOOD
Secretary
F. S. BRIEN
G. L. CASSIDY
J. M. FRIEDMAN
A. R. HACKETT
C. J. A. HALLIWELL
PROF. J. H. ILIFFE
F. D. SHANNON
P. O'M. SIMS
PROF. E. M. WALKER

1930–31

E. M. WALKER
Chairman
F. S. BRIEN
Secretary
S. J. BOCHNER
J. S. BONHAM
E. K. BROWN
M. M. CHUDLEIGH
I. W. DAVIDSON
PROF. J. H. ILIFFE
J. G. IRVING
G. K. MASTERS
C. H. RAPPAPORT
F. D. SHANNON
W. E. SHUTE
D. M. TANNER

1931–32

E. M. WALKER
Chairman
J. G. IRVING
Secretary
W. G. ARMSTRONG
J. K. BRADFORD
F. S. BRIEN
W. E. CARSWELL
H. W. FORD
A. GOGGIO
PROF. E. A. HAVELOCK
F. R. HUME
F. LASSERRE
H. MITCHELL
C. R. PARMENTER
F. D. SHANNON
L. T. WHITE

1932–33

E. M. WALKER
Chairman
F. S. BRIEN
Secretary
W. E. CARSWELL
I. R. CLEMENS
W. GARARD
A. GOGGIO
J. J. HARRIS
PROF. E. A. HAVELOCK
F. R. HUME
F. LASSERRE
C. W. MINETT
C. R. PARMENTER
J. R. SIME
M. A. WILKINSON

1933–34

PROF. E. A. HAVELOCK
Chairman
J. R. SIME
Secretary
W. E. CARSWELL
R. A. DALY
T. A. FRASER
A. GOGGIO
F. LASSERRE
D. V. LE PAN
PROF. H. R. MacCALLUM
C. W. MINETT
O. H. RUMPEL
W. G. STOBIE
H. C. WAISBERG
F. W. WOODS

1934–35

PROF. E. A. HAVELOCK
Chairman
J. R. SIME
Secretary
A. H. ARMSTRONG
W. E. CARSWELL
R. A. DALY JR.
A. GOGGIO
S. N. GOLDER
G. R. HALL
J. A. KEMP
D. V. LE PAN
W. E. CARSWELL
O. J. ROWE
F. N. SMITH

1935–36

W. E. CARSWELL
Chairman
F. N. SMITH
Secretary
A. H. ARMSTRONG
R. A. DALY
A. GOGGIO
I. E. GORDON
R. E. HAIST
A. G. KEITH
J. A. KEMP
PROF. H. R. MacCALLUM
J. B. MCDIARMID
J. E. REYNOLDS
D. M. TANNER
T. L. WIACEK

1936–37

W. E. CARSWELL
Chairman
A. H. ARMSTRONG
Secretary
D. O. BUTLER
C. K. CARRINGTON
C. B. FOSTER
A. GOGGIO
R. E. HOFMANN
E. F. HURST
L. M. LEIN
PROF. H. R. MacCALLUM
J. MCKIBBIN
F. N. SMITH
D. M. TANNER
D. K. WISE

1937–38

PROF. H. R. MacCALLUM
Chairman
A. H. ARMSTRONG
Secretary
N. R. BOWLES
T. C. DALY
C. R. DELAFIELD
F. J. HINDS
E. F. HURST
C. G. KEHLER
J. L. MCFARLAND
J. R. MILLAR
J. A. POWELL
R. G. RIDDELL
R. A. SIM
D. M. TANNER
D. J. VAN WYCK

ART COMMITTEE

1938–39

PROF. H. R. MacCALLUM
Chairman
J. W. BARNES
Secretary
W. W. ARMSTRONG
W. B. BURWELL
T. C. DALY
J. F. FREEMAN
R. S. HARRIS
F. J. HINDS
J. L. MCFARLAND
G. A. NORTHGRAVE
R. G. RIDDELL
D. M. TANNER
D. J. VAN WYCK
D. R. WARREN

1939–40

R. G. RIDDELL
Chairman
J. W. BARNES
Secretary
W. E. BURGIS
W. B. BURWELL
R. A. CLEGHORN
T. C. DALY
J. F. FREEMAN
W. B. HARPER
R. S. HARRIS
A. S. MALLON
M. A. MURPHY
W. M. NICHOLLS
D. M. TANNER
D. R. TENNENT
J. G. TODDS

1940–41

R. G. RIDDELL
Chairman
J. G. TODDS
Secretary
W. B. BURWELL
R. S. W. CAMPBELL
P. R. L. CHARLES
R. A. CLEGHORN
L. E. DOWNS
J. F. FREEMAN
P. M. GARDINER
PROF. R. E. HAIST
B. J. LEGGE
A. S. MALLON
D. E. NOEL
W. SHULMAN

1941–42

R. G. RIDDELL
Chairman
W. SHULMAN
Secretary
W. S. BROWN
PROF. C. F. COMFORT
W. S. A. DALE
T. E. DENNISON
R. C. FAIRFIELD
J. F. FLINN
P. M. GARDINER
PROF. R. E. HAIST
H. E. LEYLAND
G. R. MacDOUGALL
W. N. NICHOLLS
R. F. NOETH

1942–43

PROF. R. E. HAIST
Chairman
H. E. LEYLAND
Secretary
E. V. ABBOTT
L. E. BANKS
W. R. BENY
PROF. C. F. COMFORT
L. G. COWAN
R. R. CRANE
W. S. A. DALE
P. M. GARDINER
H. D. GRAHAM
W. M. NICHOLLS
R. C. TULLY

1943–44

PROF. R. E. HAIST
Chairman
W. R. BENY
Secretary
DR. G. H. AGNEW
J. E. ARMESTO
A. G. BROWN
G. F. Y. CHAN
W. S. A. DALE
PROF. H. N. FRYE
D. R. H. GOURLEY
W. J. MCBAIN
G. W. PHILPOTTS
C. J. SOVIE
H. F. SYLVESTER
R. C. TULLY

1944–45

PROF. R. E. HAIST
Chairman
W. R. BENY
Secretary
DR. G. H. AGNEW
J. R. BLAIS
D. A. FLOCK
PROF. H. N. FRYE
D. R. H. GOURLEY
W. N. GREER
R. B. HALL
J. O. LEE
B. S. LEVITT
R. D. LLOYD
W. M. NICHOLLS
M. OSTWALD
H. J. TOOGOOD
M. P. J. WALSH

1945–46

PROF. R. E. HAIST
Chairman
W. N. GREER
Secretary
DR. G. H. AGNEW
J. F. BAUCKHAM
V. B. BROOKS
R. G. CALVERT
E. F. COOKE
R. C. FREEMAN
PROF. H. N. FRYE
R. B. HALL
L. G. MCINTOSH
M. OSTWALD
A. L. PRIVETT
L. G. SINGER
P. F. TILLMANN

1946–47

PROF. H. N. FRYE
Chairman
W. N. GREER
Secretary
DR. G. H. AGNEW
I. BURNS
PROF. C. F. COMFORT
R. B. HALL
J. R. HARPER
J. E. HARVEY
S. H. IRVINE
R. E. RAMBUSCH
C. E. SANBORN
J. D. STENNETT
S. J. WHITE
M. S. WILSON

1947–48

PROF. H. N. FRYE
Chairman
J. D. STENNETT
Secretary
DR. G. H. AGNEW
W. C. BERNARD
P. R. BRYCE
PROF. C. F. COMFORT
R. A. FARRELL
R. B. HALL
J. R. HARPER
W. A. M. KYRO
M. A. MACKENZIE
J. G. POUPORE
M. STASICK
P. K. TAKAHASHI
S. J. WHITE
D. V. WILSON

1948–49

PROF. H. N. FRYE
Chairman
C. A. BEST
Secretary
DR. G. H. AGNEW
J. H. BARCLAY
R. L. BLOORE
P. R. BRYCE
PROF. C. F. COMFORT
P. J. A. FALQUET
D. I. GOVE
D. M. HUNTER
W. A. M. KYRO
A. I. MACRAE
D. B. STEWART
P. K. TAKAHASHI
S. J. WHITE

1949–50

PROF. H. N. FRYE
Chairman
D. B. STEWART
Secretary
J. H. BARCLAY
J. D. BOGGS
P. CHRISTENSEN
PROF. C. F. COMFORT
P. CREIGHTON
P. R. DAY
J. GRUBE
J. R. HARPER
M. H. MCLACHLAN
C. S. NOXON
R. B. SIMMINS
D. THURSTON
D. G. WATSON

1950–51

DR. C. C. LOVE
Chairman
J. D. BOGGS
Secretary
J. W. BARNES
T. D. BARNES
T. D. R. BRIANT
P. W. B. CREIGHTON
P. R. DAY
J. D. GRUBE
J. R. HARPER
J. KAMENICEK
S. KEY
M. K. MCLACHLAN
J. H. M. NIBLOCK
R. R. TOEWS
A. M. WATSON
D. G. WATSON

1951–52

DR. C. C. LOVE
Chairman
J. KAMENICEK
Secretary
J. W. BARNES
R. M. BATEMAN
T. D. R. BRIANT
R. C. CHENG
D. E. GARDNER
E. S. GIBSON
J. R. HARPER
G. A. IRWIN
W. B. KAY
S. J. KEY
W. P. SUBOCH
A. M. WATSON
D. G. WATSON
J. H. M. NIBLOCK

1952–53

DR. C. C. LOVE
Chairman
T. D. R. BRIANT
Secretary
J. W. BARNES
R. M. BATEMAN
P. C. DI NOVO
K. S. FREEDY
D. E. GARDNER
E. S. GIBSON
J. R. HARPER
J. KAMENICEK
W. B. KAY
S. J. KEY
J. G. LISTER
D. MICHEL
R. J. WIDDICOMBE

1953–54
DR. C. C. LOVE
Chairman
J. G. LISTER
Secretary
J. W. BARNES
R. M. BATEMAN
T. D. R. BRIANT
E. COOKE
T. M. DALY
P. C. DI NOVO
J. A. M. EMERSON
G. A. FIERHELLER
G. FINLEY
S. J. KEY
G. A. MCDOWELL
A. PIOTROWSKI
J. M. ROBERTS
G. P. SHEPHARD
R. M. TRILLIA

1954–55
J. HALL
Chairman
J. M. ROBERTS
Secretary
J. W. BARNES
T. D. R. BRIANT
E. COOKE
P. S. B. EZRA
G. A. FIERHELLER
G. FINLEY
A. K. GIGEROFF
T. HORI
R. J. IRVINE
J. G. LISTER
G. A. MCDOWELL
M. J. MCMORDIE
R. MOYER
S. MOSCOE
E. J. SCHONLEBER

1955–56
J. HALL
Chairman
P. J. IRVINE
Secretary
J. W. BARNES
J. A. BECKER
E. COOKE
G. S. CONN
G. FINLEY
J. GRADER
F. J. C. GRIFFITHS
J. HOFFMAN
M. JEANNERET
R. P. KAPLAN
L. G. LAWRENCE
M. MCMORDIE
N. J. P. MELNICK
C. L. TALBOT
J. N. TURNBULL

1956–57
J. HALL
Chairman
R. P. KAPLAN
Secretary
J. W. BARNES
J. A. BECKER
M. M. CASSIDY
E. COOKE
G. E. FINLEY
A. C. GRANT
F. J. C. GRIFFITHS
M. JEANNERET
H. N. J. NAGEL
D. F. PARKER
M. R. ROSS
E. J. J. RZADKI
S. TAUBE
F. S. THOMPSON
M. S. WYNSTON

1957–58
E. COOKE
Chairman
R. P. KAPLAN
Secretary
J. E. BALFOUR
J. W. BARNES
J. A. BECKER
F. J. C. GRIFFITHS
A. C. GRANT
D. GREENSPAN
J. HALL
P. W. HELLEN
K. JAFFARY
M. JEANNERET
W. R. JOHNSTON
D. S. RICHARDSON
G. P. ROSEN
M. R. ROSS
E. J. J. RZADKI
F. S. THOMPSON

1958–59
E. COOKE
Chairman
P. W. HELLEN
Secretary
T. W. BARAN
J. A. BECKER
R. B. H. DU BOULAY
J. HALL
J. E. INGLIS
M. JEANNERET
W. R. JOHNSTON
G. F. MacDONALD
C. E. MCFADDIN
D. S. RICHARDSON
M. R. ROSS
E. R. SHEPHERD
E. K. SYPESTEYN
J. P. WARD

1959–60
J. MCCULLEY
Acting Chairman
D. S. RICHARDSON
Secretary
C. C. BRODEUR
G. E. FINLEY
M. P. GRANGER
M. JEANNERET
D. J. KELLY
G. F. MacDONALD
C. E. MCFADDIN
N. PAWLEY
J. C. RUNG
J. M. SPENCE
J. F. VEIDLINGER
A. WIEDMANN
B. ZAID

1960–61
PROF. P. BUITENHUIS
Chairman
B. ZAID
Secretary
D. F. ANDRUS
L. W. BELLE
S. GELMAN
C. L. GILL
M. JEANNERET
D. J. KELLY
F. M. MCATEER
C. E. MCFADDIN
J. W. MEDLAND
G. C. NESS
N. PAWLEY
J. M. SPENCE
L. F. VALENTINE
J. T. WILBUR

1961–62

PROF. P. BUITENHUIS
Chairman
K. E. CARPENTER
Secretary
J. W. BURBIDGE
M. H. COFFENG
P. S. CULBERT
P. W. HELLEN
F. D. HOWARD
M. JEANNERET
R. T. MANKTELOW
C. E. MCFADDIN
G. C. NESS
P. G. RUSSELL
D. P. SILCOX
A. TOFF
L. F. VALENTINE
R. VASTOKAS
J. D. K. WHYTE

1962–63

PROF. P. BUITENHUIS
Chairman
J. A. BURNETT
Secretary
J. D. BOWDEN
P. B. BYRNE
D. DRACHE
P. HELLEN
R. KAPLAN
PROF. H. A. MCPHERSON
C. E. MCFADDIN
R. A. MLODZIK
G. C. NESS
D. S. RICHARDSON
J. M. ROBINSON
M. S. SHAW
M. J. SOMERVILLE
A. TOFF
T. W. TROUGHTON
F. H. ZEMENS

1963–64

PROF. H. A. MCPHERSON
Chairman
J. D. BOWDEN
Secretary
J. A. BURNETT
C. J. DINGLE
L. N. GREENSPAN
M. JOE
R. KAPLAN
C. E. MCFADDIN
J. M. ROBINSON
R. J. BOYLE
P. G. RUSSELL
D. G. SCROGGIE
M. S. SHAW
A. TOFF
M. K. WARREN
F. H. ZEMENS

1964–65

DR. H. A. MCPHERSON
Chairman
L. N. GREENSPAN
Secretary
J. D. BOWDEN
DR. P. BUITENHUIS
C. G. DUNBAR
I. M. EWING
R. KAPLAN
D. A. LEGGE
M. J. MITCHELL
T. C. MUNRO
J. ST.G. O'BRIAN
E. V. ROSEN
P. G. RUSSELL
M. S. SHAW
P. L. D. SOUTHAM
A. TOFF

1965–66

PROF. H. A. MCPHERSON
Chairman
L. N. GREENSPAN
Secretary
J. ADAMSON
J. R. BRADSHAW
DR. P. BUITENHUIS
B. CULJAT
M. K. EVANS
I. EWING
P. B. GLASS
J. G. JENKINS
N. H. MALAKIS
J. O'BRIAN
D. W. RALSTON
P. SOUTHAM
A. TOFF

1966–67

PROF. C. T. MOREY
Chairman
P. SOUTHAM
Secretary
J. ADAMSON
K. J. ALLISON
A. G. J. BRUCE
D. GOODERHAM
DR. P. M. HUGHES
N. H. MALAKIS
J. G. MARSHALL
M. MYERS
M. PETERMAN
L. K. PRENTICE
R. E. ROKOS
R. R. TAYLOR
A. TOFF
B. C. WALSH
F. H. ZEMANS

1967–68

PROF. C. T. MOREY
Chairman
R. R. TAYLOR
Secretary
G. CAMPBELL
R. J. CUNNINGHAM
C. R. FRASER
A. R. GRANT
DR. P. M. HUGHES
J. G. MARSHALL
M. J. MITCHELL
W. N. F. ORTVED
L. K. PRENTICE
G. S. REID
R. ROKOS
P. R. L. SOMERVILLE
A. TOFF
F. H. ZEMANS

1968–69

DR. P. M. HUGHES
Chairman
A. R. GRANT
Secretary
J. ADAMSON
G. R. FRASER
A. M. V. JANIKOWSKI
B. R. MCDONALD
D. D. MCKAY
D. J. MCNIVEN
DR. P. W. MELLEN
R. MELNYK
J. C. MORRIS
J. T. PIERCE
R. E. ROKOS
P. R. L. SOMERVILLE
A. TOFF
F. H. ZEMANS